Milestones of Medicine

Ruth Fox

Milestones of Medicine

Random House New York

Fifth Printing

Copyrights and Acknowledgments

Thanks are extended to the following publishers for permission to quote from books which they hold copyright:

Doubleday & Company, Inc., MADAME CURIE: A Biography, by Eve Curie, copyright 1937 by Doubleday & Company, Inc.; The Macmillan Company, PIERRE CURIE, by Madame Curie, copyright 1923 by Madame Curie; Alfred A. Knopf & Co., THE HUMAN BODY, by Logan Clendening, copyright 1927 by Alfred A. Knopf & Co.

Published in New York by Random House, Inc.
and simultaneously in Toronto, Canada by
Random House of Canada, Limited
Designed by Marshall Lee

To Mother, the *sine qua non*.

Contents

Preface

OUR cave-dwelling ancestors believed that sick people could be cured by pacifying evil spirits, demons, or departed relatives who held grudges against them. Our colony-founding ancestors believed that bleeding patients until they fainted would purge their bodies of disease.

Today in the chrome-and-white-tile-laboratory era it is easy to smile at their methods and think, "How could they have been so stupid? It's quite obvious . . ." It is obvious only after someone else has found the answers.

The road from then to now was long, dark and hazardous. Often it led into wide detours or down paths that seemed promising yet turned out to be dead ends. But from the very beginning of the journey there have been milestones along the way.

The milestones of medicine came in the shape of widely different discoveries. Some of them seemed so small that it was hardly thought necessary to record them. Others were world-shaking. Some appeared in a blinding flash of intuition and formed a part of our scientific heritage almost overnight. Still others were laboriously put together like jigsaw puzzles, each piece being added over a period of years until at the end only one fragment was needed to make the picture complete.

Here are eight of them. Among the men and women who have set these particular markers were physicists and chemists, bacteriologists and surgeons—even a pharmacist's apprentice and the captain of a sailing vessel. Some were deeply interested in research, while others simply stumbled on the answers to their problems. They had, as you will see, very little in common except this: the few hundred people who made these discoveries have seen to it that the few hundred billion of us who profit by them will lead longer and pleasanter lives.

RUTH FOX

part I

Two Gifts from the Physicists to the Doctors

1

Röntgen and the X-ray

"WILHELM!"

The bearded Professor Röntgen looked up from a thoughtful study of his shoes and said, "Hmm?" There was a frown, he noted, between the usually placid brows of his wife. "Something wrong?" he inquired, peering automatically over his shoulder to check the state of the fire. It was crackling in good order, blandly unconcerned by the bitter November wind outside.

Bertha sighed with annoyance at her husband. There he sat, drinking afternoon coffee made to his exact specifications, finishing off the best pastry to be had in the city of Würzburg, and saying nothing for an entire half hour.

"Something wrong?" the professor repeated. "Fire all right?"

Bertha stifled a strong urge to say, "Of course nothing's wrong, Wilhelm! I just love to talk to myself while you sit there like a statue of Alexander the Great!" Instead she smiled and said, "How did you like the *apfelstrudel,* Wilhelm? Did you think it was too rich?"

"Too rich?" He tugged at his beard thoughtfully. "No, I don't think so," he announced after a judicious pause. "It was excellent. In fact, I don't know that I've ever tasted better *apfelstrudel.*"

Bertha inclined her head in a gesture of deep appreciation and said, "Now that's very flattering, Wilhelm, particularly when you consider that we didn't have *apfelstrudel* today. We had cheese cake."

The rector of the University of Würzburg, the most brilliant experimental physicist of his generation, sat up straight in his chair and said weakly, "We did?" He attempted a laugh that did not quite come off.

Bertha, delighted by her victory, patted the braid which circled her pleasant face like a small domestic halo and said, "If you're thinking such interesting thoughts, Wilhelm, why don't you think them out loud?"

Röntgen laughed. "It all depends on what you mean by interesting. As a matter of fact," he added, lowering his voice confidentially, "I was thinking of cathode rays."

The term was by no means unfamiliar to his wife. In

1895 it was a matter of absolute certainty that if two physicists were in a room together, the subject of cathode rays would come up within twenty minutes. And Bertha's living room was usually cluttered with physicists.

"It seems to me," Bertha said, determined to make conversation with her husband, "that with all the talk going around about these cathode rays, somebody could tell me what they are!"

Röntgen said, "It's very complicated, and I *must* get back to the laboratory before——"

"Wilhelm! You sit right there and finish your coffee before you set foot out of this room. And talk to me!"

The professor closed and opened his eyes slowly to express an anguish of spirit that he did not feel. Even after twenty-five years of marriage, he still enjoyed the heavy-handed humor with which he dismissed his wife's occasional interest in scientific matters. He said in the singsong tone of a student recitation, "The cathode ray is the phenomenon caused by the passage of an electrical discharge through a vacuum tube."

Bertha sniffed. "What I would like to know," she said, addressing herself to her knitting, "is who started the rumor that Wilhelm Konrad Röntgen is the greatest teacher of physics in Europe!"

In reply Röntgen retreated behind his professional dignity and said, "It is now 4:03 P. M. At exactly 4:10 P. M. I shall be unlocking the door of my laboratory. Anything you can learn between now and then, you may keep without any charge by the University." He put down his coffee cup and began filling his pipe with what he considered to be seven minutes' worth of tobacco. "We can't discuss the cathode ray without mentioning vacuum tubes," he said. "And we can't speak of vacuum tubes without talking about atmospheric pressure, which brings us back to 1643."

"That should be far enough," Bertha remarked, suddenly wondering whether she would understand any of her husband's conversation.

"Galileo really started it all, though."

"Galileo?" Vague memories of her school days flitted through Bertha's mind. "Didn't he drop rocks out of a tower, or something?"

"Yes, but at the moment we're more interested in the fact that he built a pump which could drive all the air out of a glass tube. He noticed something about airless glass tubes that surprised him. No matter how often he tried it, and no matter how wide or how narrow the glass was, he found that if he put one end of the tube in water, the water always rose to the same height—about thirty-three feet. It never failed. He could demonstrate the phenomenon to anybody who asked him, but he could never explain it. People talked about an invisible suction in the tube that drew the water up. It wasn't until 1643, when Galileo had been dead for a year, that one of his pupils, a brilliant fellow named Torricelli, figured out the answer."

He rose to his feet and looked down at her solemnly.

"There wasn't any invisible suction inside the tube at all. It was the downward pressure of the air *outside* the tube that forced the water up into the vacuum. It seems clear enough to us, but in those days people hadn't really thought of air as having weight.

"Then Torricelli asked himself the big question: why did the column of water always rise to the same thirty-three-foot height? Well, that was easy enough once he had the principle worked out. The column stopped rising when the water and air were deadlocked—when the weight of air on water, and water on air, were equalized. Now how," he inquired, assuming the manner of a teacher about to ask a question which he knows the class cannot answer, "*how* do you suppose he proved it?"

Bertha shrugged. "Used something heavier than water, of course," she said, the rhythmic click-clack of her knitting needles undisturbed. "If his theory was right, then of course the heavy liquid wouldn't rise as high as the light liquid. The same weight of air would have less effect on it. Like my pushing the piano bench with all my weight, and then pushing the piano. They'd move different distances, wouldn't they?" Her tone of voice indicated that a normally bright seven-year-old could have figured it out.

The professor's dramatically pointed finger hastily retired to the underside of his beard. "Uh—yes," he said weakly. When he went on, the tone of husbandly banter was out of his voice for the first time. "So he took a glass tube, sealed at one end, filled it up with mercury, and put the open end in a bowlful of the same liquid. The column of mercury dropped immediately, but it stopped falling about thirty inches from the bowl, and there it stayed.

"Three things had happened: Torricelli's theory had been proven a fact—that's always a pleasant moment in a scientist's life; the mercury barometer had been invented; and there was a perfect vacuum in the tube between the sealed end and the top of the mercury column. And therein," he concluded with more enthusiasm than originality, "lies the tale!"

Bertha knit on and nodded encouragingly.

"The vacuum idea," Röntgen continued, slowly pacing and repacing the length of the hearth, "appealed to scientists because it puzzled them. One day—I guess it was around 1650—a clever fellow named Otto von Güricke, the Burgomaster of Magdeburg, staged an historic game with a vacuum. He built two big half-globes of copper. He polished and polished their edges, and when he put them together they formed a perfectly air-tight sphere. There was a stopcock in one side, and through it he pumped every bit of air out of the globe. Then he had the two biggest and strongest horses in town brought onto the scene. They were harnessed to opposite sides of the globe, so that they could pull in different directions. They did. They pulled harder and harder. And then harder." Röntgen made the point clear by strenuous efforts to separate the bowl of his pipe from the stem.

"Two more horses were added, then four, and still nothing happened. So there were the two copper hemispheres stuck together—but with nothing, presumably, holding them. Not until there were eight horses tugging away at each side was the globe pulled apart. The emperor, who had been invited to witness the experiment, seems to have been convinced that air is a powerful substance."

It occurred to Bertha that more than the proffered seven minutes had elapsed since her husband had begun his lecture. She glanced at her lapel watch and wondered how long it would be before she could escape to the kitchen and begin operations on the roast beef which Wilhelm had requested for dinner. She began, "Don't you think I'd better——"

"Well then," Röntgen plunged on, "for about fifty years people played tricks with vacuums." She sat back, resigned. If Wilhelm had warmed to the subject, nothing short of an earthquake would stop him before he had exhausted it. Scientists, she reflected, were just born that way.

"Then in 1705," he was saying, "Francis Hauksbee pumped the air out of a bell jar and shot electrical discharges through it—from an electric friction machine. You know what that is?"

"Certainly I know," Bertha asserted hastily, although not even the thought of an electric friction machine had ever before crossed her consciousness. Physics meant little to the domestic Bertha.

"Much to Hauksbee's surprise, flashes of purple light appeared in the jar. It was quite a moment, really; electricity and the vacuum had finally been brought together. There's no telling where that acquaintance will end."

He settled comfortably in his chair, a move which Bertha regarded as a bad sign. She thought, "Let's see—an eight-pound roast at twenty-five minutes a pound will——"

"The man who put the vacuum-tube business on a scientific basis," said Röntgen, "was Heinrich Geissler, the master glass-blower of Bonn. He made an egg-shaped vacuum globe and sealed a platinum disc inside it. That little disc brought it into the realm of pure physics. By 1878—that was the year when Sir William Crookes delivered a lecture on vacuum tubes that would have flabbergasted Torricelli and the Burgomaster—the egg was really ready for action. It had two discs in it now, an anode and a cathode—positive and negative poles, do you see?"

Bertha nodded vigorously, eager to give the impression that she saw.

"Now, when you pass electricity through such a tube, all sorts of things happen. There are more rays formed than any physicist before Crookes and his colleagues ever dreamed of. Even the pressure at which the experiments are done can change their characteristics. Crookes thought of these cathode rays almost as inhabitants of another world. There's not a physicist in Europe who hasn't done cathode-ray experiments. Lenard——" He paused long enough to snort, and then muttered, "He's at Heidelberg. Has a new experiment with cathode rays in the open air. I want to re-run them for myself and——" He stopped in mid-sentence and looked at his watch. "Do you know what time it is?" he inquired indignantly.

"Four-forty," Bertha said stoically.

"I know you'd like to hear more about this, but I must get back to the laboratory. If you have any questions, save them and I'll go on at dinner."

Bertha shuddered quietly. "Oh, I have only one question," she said patiently, "and I asked it over half an hour ago."

"You—what?"

"You've talked just beautifully," she went on, "but you still haven't answered my question, and it was really *all* I wanted to know."

"What is it, then?" the professor demanded, thoroughly confused by now.

Bertha said meekly, "What are cathode rays?"

Röntgen opened his mouth, closed it, flung up his hands eloquently and said, "Good heavens! *I* don't know! Nobody knows!" He stamped out of the room and out of the house muttering something unintelligible about women and science.

Students and faculty members alike hastily stepped aside to let the rector of the University pass without having to change his course. Respectful murmurs of, "Good afternoon, Herr Doktor," followed him down the street and up the path of the Physical Institute, on the first floor of which were his laboratories. Only one greeting, delivered by two high University officials, did he notice and acknowledge. As he opened the door he paused long enough to smile enigmatically—and disconcertingly—at the head-bobbing officials.

At that moment he had been struck by a thought which amused him. Here he was at Würzburg—the head of the great Physical Institute, the rector of the University, and so esteemed a professor that the faculty small fry hardly dared speak to him. Yet this same University of Würzburg had refused him a job as an unpaid lecturer twenty-three years ago. He was not well enough educated for the post, the University had informed him at the time. As he opened the door to his laboratory, his mind raced rapidly over the sequence of events which had combined to bring him to his present position.

Often turning points in life are brought about by trivial incidents. The long series of difficulties which the young Wilhelm Konrad Röntgen had to surmount in order first to educate himself and then find a position stemmed from the fact that one day a classmate of his had drawn an accurate caricature of a very unpopular teacher.

Wilhelm, eighteen and soon to be graduated from the Utrecht Technical School to the town's university, stood watching the artist at work.

"Here, you've given him too much hair. Move his eyebrows down a little and make his ears bigger!"

"I think it's a perfect resemblance," the artist protested, tearing the page from his notebook and hanging it up on a fire-screen. "There! How does it look now?" He stepped back, clucked in admiration, and went out of the room in search of a larger audience. Wilhelm, alone, studied the picture critically, chuckling to himself.

"Who drew that?"

Wilhelm leaped a good foot and a half off the ground, then swung around in the direction of the roar and found himself standing face to face with the subject of the artist's work. It was indeed a perfect resemblance.

"Did you draw that?"

"No, sir."

"Who did?"

The traditional code of honor of the school boy was not to be regarded lightly. Wilhelm, drawing himself up to his considerable height, announced that he had nothing to say. The headmaster was summoned. The head prefect was summoned. A faculty quorum was summoned. By the end of the day, Wilhelm, his lips still sealed, found that he was no longer a member of the student body.

Being expelled from school is never a pleasant experience. To Wilhelm, it seemed a tragic blow, for it was almost impossible to get into any Dutch or German university from the lower school without an *absolutorium,* which is equivalent to our high-school diploma.

Wilhelm's father, a prosperous merchant, was determined that the boy should go on with his studies if he wanted to do so. He called upon various influential people in town and finally arranged for Wilhelm to be given a private examination for the *absolutorium.* Young Röntgen, well prepared for the ordeal, went into it reasonably sure of himself. His confidence lasted only until he faced the board of examiners. Behind the table was an unmistakably familiar gentleman—with outsized ears and massive eyebrows. Wilhelm had not expected to see his old friend on the board of examiners, but the professor himself would not have missed the occasion for anything. Wilhelm took his examination and failed unconditionally.

To a less stubborn man this would have meant the end of his formal education, but young Röntgen determined to find a way out. He attended the University of Utrecht as a non-credit auditor, and then literally talked his way into the University of Zurich in Switzerland, a country which was less bound by academic tradition than either Holland or Germany. He spent four years in the lovely Swiss city, and at the end of them he was awarded a doctor's degree by the university.

Between classes the students liked to gather at a small inn, "The Green Glass," just around the corner from the school. The innkeeper, an educated man and a German political refugee, had a daughter named Bertha. Fräulein Ludwig was six years older than Wilhelm Röntgen, on whom she exerted the full powers of her charm. They were married in 1872, after Bertha had spent several months in Holland with Röntgen's mother, learning from her the fine points of Dutch cooking. This curious training must have been a good foundation on which to build, for once the young couple had got used to each other's eccentricities, they were happy.

It was shortly after his marriage that Röntgen applied unsuccessfully for a position at the University of Würzburg. His formal education was strangely erratic, the officials said, hardly in keeping with the traditions of the German universities. Disappointed, and aware of his new responsibilities as a family man, Röntgen removed himself and his household to the less critical University of Strassburg, as assistant to the professor of physics, Dr. Kundt.

There he gathered his forces and proceeded to show the learned men of the universities exactly what could be done by a man of "erratic training" when he put his mind to it. Paper after paper—results of experiments which amazed his older colleagues—came out of Röntgen's laboratory: forty-eight articles between 1870 and the significant 1895.

The most surprising aspect of his career, perhaps, was that Röntgen, unlike most great researchers, was also a gifted teacher. His students thought as well of him as did the administration. By 1888, sixteen years after he found his first job, Röntgen's reputation as a very great physicist was made. He was asked to fill more highly paid teaching posts than could possibly have been held by one man in a lifetime. But finally the irresistible offer came. The University of Würzburg would be pleased to have him as director of its new Physical Institute. Six years later he became rector of the university.

Even if Röntgen had done no further scientific research after that time, his name would still make its appearance in physics books and quarterlies today. The experiment, however, which was to make his name a household word on five continents began on November 8, 1895, as he removed the key from the lock of his laboratory and shut the door behind him.

The laboratory overlooked the garden of the Institute. Röntgen glanced absently out the window at the bleak little rectangle which was already encrusted with frost and then drew the blinds tightly across the panes. The test he was about to run required absolute darkness.

Strictly speaking, what he intended to do was not an experiment, from his point of view. He knew in advance what would happen. This afternoon's work involved only the process of running off Lenard's experiment as it was described in his latest paper on cathode rays.

Lenard's experiment was a straightforward one. He had built a window of thin aluminum into the side of a vacuum tube. The cathode rays formed by sparking the tube could easily penetrate this thin metal and escape to the outside. A few inches of air swallowed them up, but if one placed a little screen painted with a fluorescent salt close to the tube, the cathode rays would light it up as effectively as the rays of the sun.

It was this fluorescent effect which Röntgen wanted to see with his own eyes. His new Crookes' tube, ordered for the occasion, had been surrounded by a heavy black cardboard jacket, reinforced by tin foil, so that no light waves from the luminous tube could escape to illuminate the fluorescent screen.

"If anything but cathode rays can get out of that tube," he thought, "the experiment's no good. I'll check up on the cardboard jacket before I do anything else."

Röntgen turned off the laboratory light and then, reaching gingerly into the pitch darkness, switched on the electric current. The circuit, he noted, was all in order. He could hear the vacuum tube humming faintly as the electrical charges shot through it, but no visible light of any description came from the tube. The laboratory remained plunged in absolute darkness—except for a faint glow across the room. . . .

An optical illusion could last just so long. He closed his eyes, opened them again, rubbed them gently, and then blinked in astonishment.

It was there and it stayed there, the undeniable shimmer of light which danced in the middle of the room a few feet from the table. Mystified, Röntgen continued to pass charge after charge of electricity through the tube. The cloudy green glow persisted. He had the distinct impression that the patch of light was hanging suspended in air, but then he remembered that there was a small bench in the laboratory some three feet from the tube. All very well. There was a bench on the floor. What impulse had suddenly caused it to shine with this unearthly, incredible light?

Quickly Röntgen lit a match and stumbled across the room in the direction of the glow. He prodded it gently with his finger and found himself in contact with a very real object.

Of course! He had forgotten. The source of his ghostly glow was the little screen painted with fluorescent salt which he had prepared for the cathode-ray experiment and had tossed on the laboratory bench the day before.

Profoundly puzzled, he picked up the bench and moved it to the end of the room, as far away from the tube as the length of the laboratory allowed. Then he proceeded to recharge the tube.

Again the screen glowed. Röntgen switched on the

overhead light and looked slowly and critically from the tube to the bench and back again.

It was fantastic, but unless he had fallen asleep by the fireplace in his home, it was happening.

Röntgen accepted the phenomenon without question. Obviously something—he had no idea what—was coming from the tube, something which could pass through thick cardboard and could light up a fluorescent screen as far as six feet away. Cathode rays? Impossible. These rays were traveling twenty-five times as far as a cathode ray had ever been observed to travel. But if they were not cathode rays, what were they?

"What did you think?" a reporter asked him later.

"I did not think. I investigated!" the professor replied tartly.

The professor's lengthy investigation was interrupted by a sharp knock at the laboratory door. A servant had a concise message for the Herr Doktor from Frau Röntgen. Dinner was getting cold.

Dinner would have to wait, he announced. Dinner waited, and was eventually eaten in preoccupied silence. When he had gulped half his coffee, Röntgen muttered something unintelligible and hurried back to the laboratory.

That night and the next day and many days and nights thereafter, Röntgen spent in his darkened laboratory furthering his acquaintance with the astonishing rays. No real scientist, he knew, should ever be surprised by any phenomenon, however bizarre it seemed at first, for the universe was full of undiscovered surprises. But the rays were fantastic. Nothing he had seen in years of dealing with the oddities of nature could touch them.

There seemed no end to their determination to get out of the tube. He tried to block their passage to the screen, first with a piece of paper, then with a pack of cards, then with a book, two books, and then a sheet of aluminum. Through all these barriers the rays passed as easily as light passes through a piece of glass.

A sheet of lead finally stopped them. Placed between the screen and the tube, it "turned off" the fluorescent light at once. Röntgen allowed the rays to stub their toes on various lead objects around the laboratory and finally, for no particular reason, reached for a small lead weight on the laboratory scales. He held it up in front of the screen and turned on the current. The screen glowed furiously, except for one dark spot in the center of it.

This was to be expected. The small piece of lead had stopped the rays and cast its shadow onto the screen as any object which blocks the direct rays of the sun will cast its shadow on the ground. But as Röntgen glanced from the tube to the screen he noticed something else, something which had been unthinkable until this moment. The lead weight was not the only object casting a shadow on the screen. The hand which held the weight was there in shadow too; but it was not to all appearances a live human hand. It was a skeleton's hand. The rays had penetrated the skin but had apparently been stopped by the harder substance beneath it. For the first time a man could see—at least in shadow—the living bones in his body. Here was an eerie thought! But Röntgen was neither awed by the mysterious sight nor excited by its significance. He simply made a few entries in his notebook and went on working. And he said to himself, "I could study these phenomena more easily if I had some permanent record of them. I must see what the rays will do to a photographic plate."

During the long series of experiments which followed, Röntgen made only one recorded comment, in a letter to a friend: "I have discovered something interesting, but I do not know whether or not my observations are correct." For he had made an important decision. Whatever these rays were—and since he did not know what they were, he took to calling them X-rays—their nature seemed too different from that of other known rays for him to mention them publicly until he had gathered all possible data on them.

It was, of course, impossible to keep Bertha equally in the dark.

"Wilhelm!"

"Hmm?"

Bertha, across the dinner table, was fixing him with a long, cool stare.

"What, exactly, is going on in the laboratory?"

"Going on? What makes you think anything is going on in the laboratory?"

"I don't *think* anything is going on," she said. "I *know* something is. And what is it?"

He laughed, then sighed and said, "I'm not really sure myself, but——" He stood up and threw his napkin on the table. "Why don't you come down and see for yourself?" he asked her, much pleased with the thought that had just occurred to him.

He had been entirely right in his hunch that the X-rays might darken a photographic plate just as light darkens it. All week he had been photographing metal objects by placing them between the tube and the plate, which simply replaced the fluorescent screen. Now he remembered the sight of his skeletal hand on the fluorescent screen. Bertha wanted to know what he was doing, did she? Why, he would be glad to show her. Would Bertha be good enough to hold her hand still on a photographic plate for a few minutes?

Bertha did, while Röntgen directed fifteen minutes' worth of rays in her direction.

"There," he said at last, switching off the circuit. "That's all."

"So?" She looked unconvinced. "What——?"

"Now you must go back home and wait until I develop the plate."

Bertha raised her eyebrows skeptically and went out

into the corridor. Some hours later, her husband appeared with the developed negative, held it up to the light, and said, "There! What do you think of it?"

She looked, blinked, looked again. A skeleton's hand . . . a skeleton's hand wearing a ring . . . *her* hand?

"Wilhelm! It isn't—is it mine?"

He laughed delightedly. "I don't know who else could claim it. They're *your* bones. How do you like them?"

"Wilhelm! How frightful!"

He looked at the picture critically. "What's wrong with them? I think they're pretty." They were also the first X-ray photograph we have on record.

A few days after Christmas, Röntgen delivered to the secretary of the Würzburg Physical Society Journal a paper called simply, *On a New Kind of Rays.* "If one passes the discharges of a fairly large Ruhmkorff induction coil through a Hittorf vacuum tube . . . and if one covers the tube with a rather closely fitting envelope of thick black cardboard, one observes in a completely darkened room that a piece of paper painted with barium platinocyanide lying near the apparatus glows brightly or becomes fluorescent with each discharge. . . ."

Reprints of the historic paper were sent to friends and colleagues at the principal European universities, and to some Röntgen also sent examples of X-ray photographs. "Now," he said to Bertha, as he returned from the big yellow mailbox on the corner, "now there'll be the devil to pay!"

There was. Once that day's mail from Würzburg had been received at the various destinations, Röntgen was the most talked-about man in Europe. A few days later, when the Würzburg story had been picked up by newspapers from Vienna to San Francisco, he was the most talked-about man in the world. To his dismay he was also the most written to and the most often visited. The letters began arriving immediately—letters of inquiry, letters of congratulation, letters of disbelief, the inevitable lunatic-fringe letters upbraiding him for having released the "death rays" over a helpless world. Then reporters descended upon him, and after them came curiosity seekers. All day long expressmen lumbered in and out, delivering crate after crate of new tubes and other presumably ray-producing equipment rushed to Würzburg by alert manufacturers from all over Europe. "Our domestic peace is gone," Bertha wailed to a relative. Röntgen himself, whose personality had not changed overnight simply because he was world-famous, was amazed and not a little annoyed.

Of the early days of the experiments, he wrote to Dr. Zehnder, an old friend and co-worker: "On the first of January I mailed the reprints, and then hell broke loose! The Vienna *Neufreipress* was the first to blow the trumpet of advertising, and the others followed. In a few days I could not recognize my own work in the reports any more . . . Gradually I became used to the uproar, but the storm cost time; for exactly four weeks I was unable to make a single experiment. Other persons could work. Only I could not. You have no conception how upset things were here."

Röntgen was not overly temperamental by nature, and his annoyance with the fuss surrounding the discovery was not a pose which many men in his position might have assumed. He was irritated by the fact that only the sensational aspect of the discovery made it front-page news. For him the X-ray photographs which were suddenly rocking the world had been the means to an end, the most accurate way of recording the action of the rays.

But it is little wonder that editors the world over were saying to reporters, "Get an X-ray story for the Sunday supplement." A picture of a skull grinning from a negative was considered a shocking sight. Many who saw the photographs claimed to be oppressed by a sense of impending death for days to come. Sensitive women took to their beds. Other nervous ladies grew uneasy when men wearing eyeglasses looked at them, for they had read in the newspapers that some physicist had discovered a sort of ray or tube which could look right through the skin. Who could be sure that the rays did not come disguised in such innocent-looking equipment as ordinary spectacles? A London store made capital of the discovery with dispatch which a modern advertising agency might envy. It announced a sale of "X-ray-proof" underclothing. An otherwise unsung hero named Assemblyman Reed of Somerset County, New Jersey, introduced a bill into the State Legislature prohibiting the manufacture of X-ray opera glasses!

All this foolishness, of course, was of no real concern to Röntgen or to the scientists who regarded his work as the major achievement in years of physical research. Scientific interest in the discovery went off in two directions. The physicists, Röntgen among them, were chiefly interested in finding out the exact nature of the rays. Were they waves, in the same class as visible light? For a long time Röntgen did not believe that they were. They did nothing ordinarily expected of waves. They would neither reflect, diffract, nor show characteristic "interference phenomena." What the early experimenters did not realize was that X-rays are about one ten-thousandth the size of light waves. Using apparatus designed to test the long light waves was no more effective than using a butterfly net to sift flour. Not until ten years after the discovery was it proved conclusively that X-rays are really electro-magnetic transversal waves in the same category as visible light and ultra-violet light.

While the physicists were brooding over the problems of diffraction and reflection and interference, physicians and surgeons were enormously interested in the possibilities of the rays as a diagnostic tool. It was in bone work that the method had immediate application, for the earliest machines were not capable of photographing soft tissue. But even before the revolutionary techniques in the treatment of bone fractures had been fully exploited, engineers, chiefly in the United States, were building and perfecting powerfully volted machines which had lost all resemblance to the Hittorf-Crookes' tubes of 1895. Gradually it became clear that nearly every part of the body could be photographed by the rays. Opaque dyes were introduced into the organ to be photographed, or "fluoroscoped" in action, and other refinements continued to be made.

If the X-ray were practical for diagnosing nothing except diseases of the lung, it would still be a valuable ally of medicine. By no other means can tuberculosis be recognized in its early stages, when it is the most easily curable. Considering the National Tuberculosis Association's estimate that from sixty to ninety percent of patients now in sanitariums had no idea that they were suffering from tuberculosis until they were far advanced in the disease, the importance of the X-ray becomes clear. Wholesale, free X-ray checkups for the entire population of a city are relatively new, but they have already been proved singularly helpful means of spotting hidden cases of tuberculosis. The therapeutic value of the rays in some eighty skin disorders, and in certain types of cancer, was discovered almost immediately after the rays themselves were found.

The dependence of medicine on the theoretical sciences has never been more significantly shown than it was in the discovery of the X-ray. From the very beginning doctors realized that the physicists had given them one of the most valuable weapons ever put into the hands of their profession. Certainly it was the most unexpected.

2

Madame Curie and Radium

"EXCUSE me, Monsieur. Could you direct me to the registration office of the Faculty of Science?"

The student thus queried looked twice and said, "Follow the main corridor, Mademoiselle. Turn left at the bend." He added, "Surely you're not registering in the school yourself, Mademoiselle?", and smiled patronizingly.

She nodded shortly, then made her escape through a crowd of students milling about the entrance hall. It was the first day of the Sorbonne's winter term. Many of the students were noisily greeting old friends; some were obviously new, and awed by their presence in the oldest European university, even though the present building, which was undergoing repairs, was covered by scaffolding and hardly impressive.

"Hey, Louis!" one of the young men called out. "What's your trouble? Who's lost?"

The student collected himself, laughed, then raised a hand dramatically. "I plan to retire from the academic life," he announced sonorously, "and take up tapestry-weaving. In a word, I have now seen everything!"

"Now don't tell me the chancellor of the university has been rolling a hoop down the hall. Or has——"

"A little blonde," Louis answered cryptically, enunciating with care. "The head of a Botticelli angel, and a most charming little foreign accent. The sort of girl one imagines sitting on a velvet cushion doing needlepoint, and eating bonbons. And——"

"Where'd she go?" inquired his friend, a practical Frenchman. He looked over the crowd eagerly. "And what's she doing here?"

"She claims," the bemused Louis said, lowering his voice as though he were telling a state secret, "that she plans to study here. But I just don't believe it."

Neither did she.

Paris came as the fulfillment of a long dream, and the fair-haired young Polish girl, timidly making her way through the crowd, hardly dared to believe that she was not dreaming. How many times during the past eight years had she despaired of ever seeing the great French university, much less sitting in its lecture halls? What, after all, had been in her favor? Money? Scientific training? A wealthy patron? Influential friends?

None of these things had brought her to Paris. She had arranged the impossibility herself, with the help of only two, non-negotiable commodities: an all-exclusive love for science, and a burning ambition to study it in the City of Light which had lured so many to its schools.

Marie Skladovska was within three days of her twenty-fourth birthday on this November 3rd in 1891. Few of the naturally carefree young Parisians, who now noted her presence with nods of approval, could have guessed how hard the last years had been. From Poland to France—it had been a much longer journey than the actual thousand miles.

Science had always fascinated Marie. Her first acquaintance with the physics equipment in her father's cabinet had filled her with delight when she could barely reach its first shelf. Professor Skladovski, a physics professor in the Warsaw public schools, was a widower who had faced the problem of raising and educating his four children on the pathetically small salary accompanying his title. He had seen more than one of the cruel useless revolutions by which Poland had tried to throw off the domination of Russia. And now his children were growing up at a time when it was against the law for a Polish teacher in Warsaw to speak to Polish children in the Polish language.

Marie's school days were not entirely happy ones. The youngest Polish children knew that for every word said to them their teachers were responsible to a Russian director of education who, in turn, was watched by the Russian secret police. Even the satisfaction of being the acknowledged head of the class had its unpleasant side, for Marie knew that whenever the detested Russian inspector came to call it would be she whom the nervous teachers would order to recite for him.

The girl's early determination to study in Paris was by no means a whim. It was a matter of necessity. When she graduated from high school, taking all the medals and prizes with her, she had all the education which her native city could offer. Women were not allowed to attend the University of Warsaw. Higher education for Polish girls was almost unheard of. With her older sister, Bronislava, who wanted to study medicine, Marie plotted romantic, impossible plans. They would get to Paris some day, somehow, the girls vowed. They were not sure when. They certainly did not know how. And then, the problem closest at hand was not going to Paris. It was getting a job in Warsaw.

How did a poor but well-born young lady secure a position in those days? The respectable jobs open to women could be counted on the fingers of one hand. Tutoring the children of rich families was the least objectionable. Marie and her sister took up the wearisome business with tight-lipped determination to make a success of it.

Their enthusiasm gave way after one year's experience. They were not the only girls, they found, who had elected the ungrateful work as a means of livelihood. At times it seemed that there were more available tutors than there were rich, privately educated pupils.

Marie had always had a realistic approach to the problem of living. "Listen, Bronya, you know perfectly well that if we wait until both of us have enough money to go to Paris, neither one of us will ever see the inside of the Sorbonne."

"But how else can we——?"

"I've already decided," her younger sister interrupted. "You must go to Paris alone. I can make twice as much money as I earn now by taking a position as governess with some rich family. I can send you half my salary and save the rest. Then when you're a doctor and making money yourself, I'll come to Paris and you can help me."

"But——" Bronya began, sputtering. Marie had a way of making shattering announcements as though she were announcing the time of day. "How can you even think of such a thing? How can you——"

"Because," Marie said, her forehead wrinkled, "if we don't do *something* desperate, we'll die no more educated than we are today!" She paused eloquently. "And that's just—well, it's just impossible."

Her mind once made up was seldom unmade. Bronya began looking up trains for Paris.

It had been a logical decision, but it had been a cruel one. Although Marie pretended the greatest enthusiasm for the idea until her sister was safely out of Warsaw, the thought of the long, dull years ahead chilled her heart. Governess in a wealthy family! Neither friend nor servant . . . an undefined social position to which one adhered more by instinct than by rule. All wealthy families, the zealous young revolutionary told herself, were bound to consist of stupid people with dull children. She remembered some of the specimens she had tutored, and shuddered.

After a few trials and errors, Marie accepted a position on a country estate located in a district with the rustic name of Plock. One could surely save money in a village called Szczuki, she thought. How could one possibly spend it? And the saving of money had become the most important activity of life. Bronya, in Paris, was leading the Spartan existence of a poor student in the Latin Quarter. Professor Skladovski would have to retire the next year, by official regulation, and the family income would suffer a drastic cut. Her savings —those few roubles which she had squeezed out of each month's salary—were synonymous with her future. With a heavy heart, she said good-bye to her father and set out for Plock.

To her relief she found that life in the country was far less burdensome than she had expected it to be. Her employers were pleasant people; her ten-year-old pupil could possibly have been more spoiled than she was. On the whole, Marie was pleased with the place, although in her letters to fellow-reformers at home, she could not refrain from a few severe comments on the customs of the landed gentry.

"In this part of the country nobody works," she wrote. "People think only of amusing themselves; and since we in this household keep a little apart from the general dance, we are the talk of the countryside . . . There was a ball here on Twelfth Night. I was treated to the sight of a certain number of guests worthy of the caricaturist's pencil, and enjoyed myself hugely. The young people here are most uninteresting. Some of the girls are so many geese who never open their mouths; the others are highly provocative . . ."

To Marie, the only important hours of the day were the short periods which she could spend with the books which she had brought along to share her exile. "At nine in the evening," she wrote to a friend, "I take my books and go to work, if something unexpected does not prevent it . . . I have even acquired the habit of getting up at six so that I work more—but I can't always do it . . . A very nice old man is staying here just now, and Mme. Z. asked me to ask him to teach me how to play checkers—to amuse him. I also have to make a fourth at bridge, and that drags me away from my books . . . I read several things at a time: the consecutive study of a single subject would wear out my poor little head which is already much overworked. When I feel myself quite unable to read with profit, I work problems of algebra or trigonometry, which allow no lapse of attention and get me back on the right road." On such studies as these, she was laying the foundations for her future.

The placid, monotonous pattern of life was soon broken. An older son of the family returned from the University of Warsaw for his summer holiday. In the best tradition of older sons of wealthy families during vacations, he promptly fell in love with the beautiful, romantically poor governess. The eighteen-year-old Marie was intrigued by the young student. Her textbooks of physics, and even the trigonometry problems which had served as relaxation, became less and less appealing. Paris itself grew dim. Was it possible, she asked herself, that her destiny, which she had expected to find only in Paris, had really been waiting for her here in Plock? When she agreed to marry the rich young man, she was filled with a vague relief. No more Paris? Why, what a crushing weight off her overburdened shoulders.

Reality was not long in asserting itself. The question which Marie imagined she had settled was as uncertain as before.

"For heaven's sake, Casimir! You can't be serious!"

"But Mother, I—I thought you liked Marie. I

thought——" A fumbling reply, but then Casimir was a fumbling young man.

"My *dear* boy!" his mother said patiently. She had secretly been expecting something like this. "My dear boy, certainly I like her. I like the parlor maid, too. And I'm particularly attached to the chambermaid. That hardly means that I'd approve of your *marrying* one of them!"

"But Mother, how can you——"

"Really, Casimir, you surprise me. A charming, intelligent girl, of course. Irreproachable character. Otherwise she wouldn't be your sister's tutor. But as to marrying her! An *employee*! It's not worth discussing, and please don't let your father get wind of it. One shudders to think what it would do to his arteries!"

"I—I suppose you must be right, Mother."

"Mother's always right, dear." She smiled. "Why, when I think of the hundreds of girls who would give *anything* to marry into this family, I——" She shrugged, then concluded, "Really, I don't know what you could have been thinking of to pick out an absolute nobody."

On second thought, neither could he. And that was that.

Although Marie complained to no one, her far from idyllic first love had been a shock to her sensitive heart. But the end result was a good one. The old ambition flared up, stronger than it had ever been.

She wrote to one of her friends, "Some people pretend that in spite of everything I am obliged to pass through the kind of fever called love. This absolutely does not enter into my plans. If I ever had any others, they have gone up in smoke; I have buried them; locked them up; sealed and forgotten them—and you know that walls are always stronger than the heads which try to demolish them . . ."

One wonders whether this family from Plock, some of whom might be living today, ever realized that if it had not been for their fortunate snobbery, Marie Skladovska might never have gone to Paris and become Madame Curie.

Paris! How far away it seemed to her the day she wrote to her brother: "I am going to stick the last stamp I possess on this letter, and since I have literally not a penny—not one!—I shall probably not write to you again until the holidays, unless by some chance a stamp should fall into my hands . . . My darling Jozio, if you only knew how I sigh and long to go to Warsaw for only a few days! I say nothing of my clothes, which are worn out and need care —but my soul too is worn out. Ah, if I could extract myself for just a few days from this icy atmosphere of criticism, from the perpetual guard over my own words, the expression on my face, my gestures. . . . If I only didn't have to think of Bronya I should present my resignation to the Z's this very instant and look for another post, even though this one is so well paid."

Another year of this unenviable existence passed by, then a second year, a second set of employers, a third year—and then a glimmer of hope. Bronya was engaged to a medical student and planned to marry him immediately after his graduation. She herself had only one more year of studies to complete before she could begin practicing. Now she would have a home, and her first thought was for the sister who had made such sacrifices for her. "And now you, my little Manya," she wrote, "you must make something of your life sometime. If you can get together a few hundred roubles this year, you can come to Paris next year and live with us, where you will find board and lodging. . . . You must take this decision; you have been waiting too long. I guarantee that in two years you will have your master's degree. Think about it; get the money together; put it in a safe place. And *don't* lend it!"

It was impossible. But it was really happening. In October of 1891, Marie left Warsaw on the Paris express, fourth class.

What a revelation Paris was! The commonplaces of its everyday life seemed almost miraculous to the Polish girl. Here one could speak any language, could read any book, could stand on the street corner loudly expressing opinions which at home would have turned every thought to Siberia. For the first time in her life, she was completely happy. Happiness on a hundred francs a month (less than twenty dollars), which paid for lodging, food, university fees, and books, clearly did not depend on the usual standards. A diet of bread, tea, radishes, and a rare, occasional egg, was no more conducive to ordinary contentment than was the icy little attic in which she lived. The comfort which she could have enjoyed in the home of her sister, she had given up soon after her arrival. In her own room, she felt, she could study with less distraction. Every second which she spent with anything but physics and mathematics seemed an irreplaceable loss.

What did it matter to her that on winter nights she was too cold to sleep until she piled every piece of clothing, every scrap of carpet, even the movable furniture onto her bed? In the morning she would be back in the lecture hall, listening to the voices of the great scientists whose names she had revered for years. And most wonderful of all, she would be back in the laboratories of the Sorbonne, her head bent for hours of affectionate labor over an electrometer or a spectroscope, the fair, much-admired hair all disheveled.

To her colleagues, *la belle Polonaise* was a complete enigma. She permitted the comradeship of only a handful. She gave her friendship to fewer still. Love? It simply did not exist in her scheme of things. Dedication to one's chosen field was no novelty at the Sorbonne, which from its twelfth century beginnings had sheltered the great scholars of all ages and all countries. But not within the experience of the present faculty had any student in the department lived so exclusively for work as this beautiful young girl with the difficult last name. It was no surprise to anyone except Marie when she passed the master's examination in physics, first in the class.

Although she had always intended to return to Poland as soon as she had her degree, Marie decided to stay in Paris for one more year. The abstract world of mathematics was too alluring to let go. In the fall she began working toward her second master's degree and working also on her first job.

During the summer, a Polish scientific society had commissioned her to do some research on the magnetic properties of certain steels. The commission was both gratifying and profitable, but Marie was hampered by the lack of adequate laboratory space. She complained of her difficulty to a countryman, Professor Kovalski, who was in town combining a Parisian honeymoon with a physics convention.

"I have a friend," he told her, "who teaches in the School of Physics and Chemistry in Rue Lhomond. It may be that he can help you—either with laboratory space or advice or both. Have tea with us tomorrow and meet him."

Marie agreed.

"Upon entering the room I perceived, standing framed by the French window opening on the balcony, a tall young man with auburn hair and large, limpid eyes," she was to write. "I noticed the grave and gentle expression of his face, as well as a certain abandon in his attitude, suggesting the dreamer absorbed in his reflections. He showed me a simple cordiality and seemed to be very sympathetic. After that first interview he expressed the desire to see me again and to continue the conversation of that evening on scientific and social subjects in which he and I were both interested, and on which we seemed to have similar opinions."

Although this was the first time that Marie had ever met Pierre Curie, his name was not unfamiliar to her. It was a name of which a student of physics would naturally be aware. The "Curie scale," the "Curie electrometer," "Curie's law"—it was in these connections that Marie knew the great physicist. Neither the Polish student nor the French professor had, of course, any notion that the little tea-party which brought them together would one day produce a great scientific collaboration.

Pierre Curie found himself first startled, then captivated by this young woman who conversed with ease and animation on magnetism, piezoelectricity, and the symmetry of crystalline substances. It was a unique experience. The physicist realized almost at once that he would eventually marry Marie Skladovska, but it took him over a year to convince the stubborn girl, although he began trying promptly.

"We met again at the Physics Society and in the

laboratory. Then he asked if he might call on me. I lived at that time in a room on the sixth floor of a house situated near the schools . . . Pierre Curie came to see me, and showed a simple and sincere sympathy with my student life. Soon he caught the habit of speaking to me of his dream of an existence consecrated entirely to scientific research, and he asked me to share that life. It was not, however, easy for me to make such a decision, for it meant separation from my country and my family, and the renouncement of certain social projects dear to me. Having grown up in an atmosphere of patriotism kept alive by the oppression of Poland, I wished, like many other young people of my country, to contribute my effort toward the conservation of our national spirit."

Marie decided rationally to give up Paris and Pierre Curie. To her surprise and irritation, she soon found that her heart had not the slightest intention of agreeing. She compromised by telling herself that although she did not mean to marry Pierre Curie, or anyone else, it might do no harm to remain in Paris for just one more year. The emotional conflict must have affected her work. She took her examination for the master's degree in mathematics, and could only pass second in the class.

Marie left for home, half promising to return, but giving Pierre no consolation for her absence better than an offer of friendship. Unhappy after her departure, Pierre turned his leisure to good advantage, for the charming letters which he wrote were a constant reminder to the girl that she too was lonely that summer.

"We have promised each other—haven't we?—to be at least great friends? If only you will not change your mind! For there are no promises that are binding; such things cannot be ordered at will. It would be a fine thing, just the same, in which I hardly dare believe, to pass our lives near each other, hypnotized by our dreams: your patriotic dream, our humanitarian dream, our scientific dream."

In the fall he resumed his suit at first-hand, for Marie was back in Paris— "only for a year." Not until that July did she realize that she was finally, happily defeated. "But what am I to do?" she wrote to a friend at home. "Fate has made us deeply attached to each other and we cannot endure the idea of separating."

Those who knew the two well could have predicted the details of their wedding: Marie in a navy-blue wool suit; a few minutes before an official at City Hall; no exchange of rings, no wedding breakfast; and finally a trip on two beautiful, shining new bicycles, the young couple's gift to each other. It was a wonderful summer. It was, Marie decided, going to be a wonderful life.

The new Madame Curie was an inexperienced housewife, but she had never yet failed to master any study to which she put her mind. The mysteries of the kitchen occasionally baffled the future Nobel prize winner in chemistry. A batch of jelly which "jelled" was almost as satisfying to her as turning out a successful experiment.

Life was suddenly good to them. "I have got a wife made expressly for me, to share all my preoccupations," Pierre Curie announced gleefully to a friend.

"I have the best husband one could dream of . . . He is a true gift of Heaven, and the more we live together the more we love each other," Marie wrote to her sister.

Soon after the birth of Irène, her first child, Marie, although she was scarcely able to walk, began to make serious plans for her doctor's dissertation. The time which she would have to spend on the work was too valuable to be disposed of lightly. She looked around for a piece of original research in a field that had not been covered too thoroughly already.

When M. Becquerel was excited, M. Becquerel's little white beard vibrated with emotion. At the moment, M. Becquerel was very much excited. Marie wondered whether the explosive Frenchman would succeed in knocking any glassware from her laboratory table before he finished the story he was just beginning. Both she and her husband had left their work and were patiently listening to the rolling phrases of their good friend.

"Well then," M. Becquerel was saying, "you know that off and on since 1895 I have been studying fluorescent substances?"

It was a rhetorical question. Few physicists had *not* been studying fluorescent and phosphorescent bodies since 1895. The chance observations which the rector of the University of Würzburg had made in November of that year had stirred up a scholarly buzz in the laboratories of four continents. A study of fluorescent and phosphorescent bodies was a natural by-product of Röntgen's discovery.

It had been known for years that certain bodies, after exposure to light, give off spontaneous rays. Minerals which stop reacting as soon as the light is removed are called fluorescent; those which continue to glow even after the light is taken away are known as phosphorescent. And for as many years as it had been observed, scientific minds had wondered about the mysterious, unworldly light that was seen in some natural ores. Not until Röntgen's discovery of the X-ray had any clue to its identity been offered. But now . . . Could it be that phosphorescence was somehow related to the emanations from Röntgen's vacuum tube? The possibility provided limitless opportunities for the ambitious French scientists. Henri Becquerel, now pacing the floor of the Curies' laboratory, was the most ambitious of them all.

"So eventually," he was saying, "I get around to studying uranium salts. I ask myself—will uranium ore have any effect on a photographic plate? It's not a very serious question, but I have a few free minutes one Sunday and I decided to try it. In the middle of my experiment, what happens? What *always* happens when a man is trying to work on a quiet Sunday? Visiting relatives!" He snorted eloquently. "So I wrap the ore in a piece of black paper and toss it and the photographic plate into a drawer. And then I go listen to my fine second cousin discourse on the perils of the millinery business. Pah! No scientist should attempt to——"

"What happened to the experiment?" Marie asked, wondering how long the old gentleman intended to linger.

"Ah, that's why I'm here," he said, dismissing his relatives with a pound on the table. "What happened? Just this. A few days later, I opened the drawer and saw the ore sitting there, ever so peacefully, on the photographic plate. I suddenly think, 'What harm would it do if I just develop that plate?' Then I say, '*Hein?* What *good* will it do?' But at such moments——" He considered his words carefully. "At such moments I always find it wiser to follow my instinct and ignore the logic. I developed the plate. Do not ask me why." He shrugged off his lack of logic with some degree of pride.

"Did it——?" Marie began.

"In the center of the plate," the old man went on, "is a fogged area—as though just so much of the plate had been exposed to light. The rest? Not a trace of exposure. I say to myself, '*Bon,* the uranium was unwrapped for a few minutes. It picked up some light. I threw it into the drawer. It gave off light for a few minutes like any good phosphorescent body.' "

"Through black paper?" Marie inquired.

"So I said," he went on. "Through heavy black paper? We shall see." He leaned over and shook a finger in the young woman's face. "I said to myself, 'Let us give this uranium a good chance to perform and see what it can really do!' I wrapped it up in the heaviest black paper I could find. I put it in the darkest drawer, in the darkest corner of my laboratory. Any little phosphorescence would be gone in a few hours. But one thing and another comes up, and I do not return to the uranium for a whole month. Now there is no question of external light. Any effect it has on a photographic plate is its own responsibility. *Bon.* Again I put it on a photographic plate. Again I develop the plate." He paused impressively, then ripped the paper from the large, rectangular package he had brought into the laboratory with him. Silently he handed it to Pierre Curie.

A small area in the center of the plate had been exposed to light—an area shaped like a good-sized chunk of ore.

"Incredible," Pierre Curie murmured, half to himself. "If anyone but you had done this experiment——"

"Oh, there's no question about it," Becquerel said. "The ore and nothing but the ore caused that exposure—just like the Röntgen ray, you see."

"But *not* just like the Röntgen ray, not at all!" Marie protested. "The Röntgen ray is produced by a careful arrangement of electricity acting on a vacuum tube. These rays are simply present in a natural ore! A natural ore giving off invisible radiance that has nothing to do with absorbed light. And this—this——" she hesitated over the word, "radioactivity is strong enough to expose a plate even through double wrappings of black paper."

Not until much later in their conversation did anyone realize that a brand new word had just been added to the universal language of science.

Marie was delighted by Becquerel's discovery for personal as well as scientific reasons. It solved the problem of her dissertation automatically. In her most optimistic mood she had never expected to find such a superb topic. The field was absolutely untouched. It was work to be done exclusively in the laboratory. There was nothing to look up, no hints to be taken from the works of older and wiser scientists. The complete bibliography of uranium data consisted of the few short papers in which Henri Becquerel communicated his discovery to his scientific colleagues.

Marie gathered together her equipment and went to work—in a laboratory which had no claim to the name except her presence there. The School of Physics and Chemistry in which her husband taught had consented to let her use an abandoned storeroom. Here both she and her sensitive apparatus suffered the extremes of cold and dampness, but such inconveniences were nothing new to Marie, and she began her experiments with an enthusiasm she had not felt since her first days in Paris.

As her familiarity with the uranium rays grew, Marie permitted herself to draw one definite conclusion about them. They were produced in exact proportion to the amount of uranium in the ore under observation. The chemical combination in which the uranium occurred? It was a matter of complete indifference to the rays. And how completely the pattern of her work was to be disrupted by that indifference!

Radiation was a property of the uranium atom itself. But what reason did she or anyone else have to assume that it was the property only of the uranium atom? This would be her special problem to investigate, she decided. She wondered whether the change in her plans would come as a shock to Pierre. It was easy enough to lead into the subject at the right moment. Talk about her work formed much of the light conversation as well as the serious talk around the house.

"*How* people will go on!" Pierre himself went on one evening. "I can just hear them! 'Do you see that pretty little woman wheeling the baby-carriage? She's the author of a work called "Observations on the

Radioactive Properties of Uranium Ores, with Special Reference to——' ' '"

"But that's not the title any more!" Marie interrupted him.

"Ah well, we can make it longer if we try. No dissertation title worth its salt should be shorter than——"

"What I mean," she said incisively, "is that I'm not making a study of radioactive properties of *uranium.* I'm making a study of radioactive properties as they might exist in all the elements."

Pierre Curie smiled with no surprise, as he had thought all along that she would eventually reach such a decision. "At last count," he said in a tone of mock terror, "there were seventy-eight of them."

Seventy-eight. But she could dismiss the majority after only a few weeks' investigation. Only two of the seventy-eight were found to be radioactive: uranium, as she knew, and thorium, an element discovered in 1829 by the great Swedish chemist Jöns Berzelius. Strictly speaking, she had completed the original mission. She had found out that two elements were radioactive, that seventy-six were not. The information did not begin to satisfy her. She was consumed by curiosity about the nature of radioactivity. In her desire to learn all she could about the phenomenon—her phenomenon, so far, almost exclusively—she investigated every bit of uranium or thorium ore she could get her hands on. It was thus that she first made the acquaintance of Bohemian pitchblende.

Pitchblende is a crude uranium ore abundant in the mountain region of what is now western Czechoslovakia. It was a convenient compound with which to work, because its chemical composition had been accurately established. Marie knew in hundredths of a percent exactly how much uranium and thorium each sample of ore contained.

"I *thought* I did, anyway," she said to herself, frowning darkly at an innocent-looking fistful of pitchblende. The first day's work with the new ore had been full of surprises, the kind of surprises which scientists find irksome. Her laboratory equipment simply refused to do what was expected of it. By the end of the day, Marie was convinced that she had bungled her chemical analysis of the ore as badly as such an uncomplicated operation could be bungled.

It all seemed wrong. Pitchblende contained a certain amount of uranium and a certain amount of thorium. Therefore its radiations should be producing a predictable effect on the electrometer by which she measured radioactivity. What the ore was actually doing was fantastic. It had the highest degree of radioactivity she had ever seen recorded by an electrometer. It was an incredibly strong producer of radiation, this Bohemian pitchblende. But why? Certainly not because of the polite dash of uranium and thorium she had found in it.

Obviously, she concluded, there was only one explanation. She had made a mistake. She began again, with a new sample. This time she determined the chemical composition of the ore with a precision that would gladden the heart of any good chemist. Then she measured its radioactivity.

Still the figures were out of line, and still she refused to accept the possibility that she was right. Sample after sample of pitchblende passed through her tests, which were now fanatically precise. Her figures were checked and rechecked by Pierre. In time, it became impossible to doubt their accuracy.

There was not enough uranium and thorium in pitchblende to account for the degree of radioactivity it showed. But no other element known was radioactive. What, then, was the source of this abundant radiation in pitchblende?

For a scientist with so logical a mind there was only one answer. She had discovered another element.

Pierre Curie considered the odds against which his wife was struggling in this staggering new development in her work, and willingly gave up his current researches on crystalline structures. They became collaborators. The same problem which had hounded Marie from her earliest days as a researcher now faced them both. Where were they to work? Pierre Curie was one of the most esteemed of all living physicists —outside France. But he knew that if he petitioned the government and waited for a subsidy, the work would never even be started. The Third Republic was notoriously snarled in red tape. Not even the officials of the Sorbonne thought the project important enough to warrant lab space.

The last resort was the school in Rue Lhomond, where Marie's drafty little workroom was located. Her window looked out on a courtyard behind the main building. At one end of the yard there was an old shed—abandoned because of its unfitness to hold either the living or the dead. It had once been used to store the cadavers used by the medical students from the University. But in view of its sagging roof, its dirt floor, its easy access to wind, dust, rain and snow, the cadavers had been moved to a better home. The shed was vacant and possession was ceded to the Curies.

The second problem of the two scientists was source material. Pitchblende was fantastically expensive for their limited purses, as were all ores of uranium, which in those days was used in the manufacturing of fine glass and porcelain. Not in their wildest flights of fancy could the two conceive of going on with the work if they had to buy pitchblende out of their own incomes.

But this obstacle was no match for them. "Surely," they reasoned, "the ore is of no use to anyone after the uranium has been extracted. And the uranium in it is of no use to us, but is just an extra step in the separation process."

By good fortune they knew a man who knew a man who knew a man . . . Soon word came from the directors of the St. Joachimstal mines in Bohemia that one complimentary ton of pitchblende residue was on its way to Paris, express collect. The mine had no further use for it, and could not imagine why the odd Monsieur and Madame Curie of Rue Lhomond wanted it, but was glad to be of service.

One ton of dirt . . . a broken-down shed . . . a large iron cauldron . . . Around these things four years of their life would revolve.

Their procedure was simple enough in principle. First, by the established methods of chemical analysis, they separated all the metallic groups in the ore, measuring the radioactivity of each group as they went; they discarded the inactive groups, and then began separating the active ones. Thus, slowly, but unerringly, they closed in on the producer of the powerful radiation—element X.

How wrong they had been to assume that from now on, nothing about radioactivity could surprise them! They soon found that two groups, the known elements of which were not radioactive, showed considerable radiation. One of the unknowns was separated out of the ore in the company of bismuth. Although its complete isolation was some years away, they were certain enough of its existence to give it a name. A name for a new element, for one of the building blocks of the universe! Marie knew without hesitation how she would dispose of this rare gift.

To the *Proceedings of the Academy of Science* for

July, 1898, the Curies communicated as follows: "We believe the substance we have extracted from pitchblende contains a metal not yet observed, related to bismuth by its analytical properties. If the existence of this new metal is confirmed we propose to call it *polonium,* from the name of the original country of one of us."

The other new element clung to the barium which was removed from the ore. The Curies soon realized that this unknown was the strongest radioactive substance that had ever been measured by their electrometer. As they uncovered more and more proof of its tremendous activity, their hearts sank, for the greater its powers of radiation, the smaller the quantity of the element needed to produce the radiation. It was like looking for the proverbial needle in a haystack. How did one go about finding this minutely small needle in a ton of brown dirt? In any case, Marie decided, since this element was probably the most radioactive on the face of the earth, she would name it accordingly. Long before she actually saw it, she called it radium.

"In our opinion," Marie wrote later, "there could be no doubt of the existence of these new elements, but to make chemists admit their existence, it was necessary to isolate them." Radium, they soon discovered, would be easier to separate from barium than polonium from bismuth. Since it was also the more radioactive of the two, they decided to concentrate on it for the time being. While Pierre devoted himself to delicate researches on the nature of the radium rays, Marie elected the jobs nearest to her heart: isolating the element from its ore and determining its atomic weight, which alone would prove its existence to the skeptical chemists.

"We were very poorly equipped with facilities for this purpose," she wrote. "It was necessary to subject large quantities of ore to careful chemical treatment. We had no money, no suitable laboratory, no personal help for our great and difficult undertaking. It was like creating something out of nothing, and if my earlier student years had once been called by my brother-in-law the heroic period of my life, I can say without exaggeration that the period on which my husband and I now entered was truly the heroic one of our common life."

In the Curies' shed there was nothing resembling even the simple equipment found in the chemistry laboratory of almost any school. Among other things, they had no hood to carry off the noxious fumes produced by parts of the separation process. That disastrous lack presented no problem to Marie. Midsummer or mid-winter, she moved her iron cauldron into the courtyard, built a fire under it, and carried on operations out of doors. "Sometimes I had to spend a whole day mixing a boiling mass with a heavy iron rod nearly as large as myself," she wrote. "I would be broken with fatigue at the day's end."

As the ton of pitchblende diminished, and the unwanted metals in it were discarded one by one, more subtle difficulties replaced the mere unpleasantness of hard physical labor. In the separation of radium from barium, Marie engaged in the most delicate chemical operations she had ever attempted. Now more than ever before she found it hard not to be bitter about the working conditions of her "laboratory." The dirt and coal dust which flew in the window with every puff of wind filled her heart with despair. How many times had she completed a difficult, tedious step in the fractional-crystallization process, only to have the day's work rendered useless by a stray blast of coal dust which had filtered in!

It was a hard, often a cruel life they had chosen for themselves, but Marie was later to look back with nostalgia to the burdensome days they spent in the wretched shack. "We were very happy in spite of the difficult conditions under which we worked," she wrote. "We passed our days at the laboratory, often eating a simple student's lunch there. A great tranquillity reigned in our poor, shabby hangar; occasionally, while observing an operation, we would walk up and down talking of our work, present and future. When we were cold, a cup of hot tea, drunk beside the stove, cheered us. We lived in a preoccupation as complete as that of a dream."

Four years after it had begun, the search ended. From forty-eight months of inspired stubbornness and a ton of pitchblende, Marie extracted—literally forced—one decigram of radium salt. Three-tenths of an ounce! She said, "At last the time came when the isolated substances showed all the characteristics of a pure chemical body. This body, the radium, gives a characteristic spectrum, and I was able to determine for it an atomic weight much higher than that of the barium. This was achieved in 1902. I then possessed one decigram of very pure radium chloride. It had taken me almost four years to produce the kind of evidence which chemical science demands, that radium is truly a new element. One year would probably have been enough for the same purpose, if reasonable means had been at my disposal. The demonstration that cost so much effort was the basis of the new science of radioactivity."

The sight of the pure product was a thrilling experience. Many times during those tranquil conversations of which Marie speaks so lovingly they had wondered what the salts of the metal would look like. Copper, cobalt, nickel and many other metals combined in salts of beautiful coloring. Perhaps, Pierre Curie had once suggested hopefully, radium would be as satisfactory. The salts which finally could be observed were beautiful beyond all expectations. They gave off light spontaneously, so that at night the ugly old shed in the Rue Lhomond was transfigured. "We then perceived on all sides the feebly luminous silhouettes of the bottles of capsules containing our products," Marie described the spectacle. "It was really a lovely sight and one always new to us. The glowing tubes looked like faint fairy lights."

By the summer of 1903, radium was a famous word in every country on earth. There was only one small detail related to her work for which Marie, in the rush of events, had not yet found time. On June 25th, the Faculty of Science of the Sorbonne met to examine a candidate for the doctor's degree. The title of the dissertation, after all, was short: "Researches on Radio-active Substances," by Marie Skladovska Curie. The academic ceremony was a simple one, its procedure and formulae following the tradition of seven hundred years. . . . "The University of Paris grants you the title of doctor of physical science. . . ."

How many of the people present on that occasion realized the full significance of what the timid, low-voiced candidate was saying to her professors? Perhaps not more than two. A gifted imagination was required to understand that in the process of fulfilling her old ambition toward this degree, the Polish girl had up-rooted the most fundamental of all existing concepts on the nature of the physical universe.

The axioms were suddenly found to be errors. The fixed, indivisible atom? The permanent, unalterable element? What had become of them? All over the world research physicists, recovering from the first shock of the news from Paris, proceeded to rewrite their textbooks.

The rays which had developed a photographic plate and provoked Marie Curie's investigations were passed through a magnetic field and found to consist of three distinct varieties of emanation. They were labelled alpha, beta, and gamma. The gamma rays proved to be identical with the X-ray of the cathode tube. The beta rays are electrons—particles charged with units of negative electricity streaming from the nucleus of the atom at a rate closely approaching the speed of light. The alpha rays are fast-moving atoms of helium.

The radioactive elements were found to be family groups, one member forming through the spontaneous degeneration of another. A fantastic discovery, this, incredible beyond the wildest dream of a medieval alchemist. A uranium atom, the physicists now found, expels three atoms of helium and two electrons on a rigidly exact time schedule, and thus becomes a radium atom; from radium comes radon, the newly discovered member of the inert gas family; from radon comes polonium; and, as end product of the fourteen changes in the series, from polonium comes lead. Now it was clear why ores of uranium are invariably found to contain lead. Transmutation of the elements was not a myth, after all. The years between 1900 and 1904 were exciting ones in the history of science.

The laws governing the constant rate of disintegration were established by Lord Rutherford, the British physicist who had done pioneer work on the nature of the rays. He calculated that for a given amount of uranium to convert one half of its mass into radium, 4,670,000,000 years are required; for radium to lose half its weight, 1690 years must pass; for polonium to follow suit, 136 days.

To their dismay, radium made its discoverers famous. The nature of the work would have drawn the attention of the world to the discoverers no matter who they had been. But that one of them should be a woman! In 1900 this fact came as such a shock that most people found it far more incredible than any single fact about radioactivity.

The Curies found themselves the most talked-about people in the world, like Röntgen before them. Their house was besieged by newspapermen, by photographers, by autograph and souvenir hunters. Röntgen had attracted attention, but he, after all, was a bearded university man, not a beautiful young mother. Their fame puzzled the unhappy Curies. Marie, who had said and would say so often, "In science one should be interested in things, not people," was embittered by this development. What disturbed her profoundly was the fact that no aid was given them. While morning editions were telling their readers "exclusive" stories about what Monsieur and Madame Curie had said, done, or worn the evening before, Monsieur and Madame Curie were still fighting against poverty, were still working with inadequate laboratory space and equipment, were still spending their precious daytime hours teaching school in order to eat.

Temporary relief from their financial difficulties eventually came. But it came from Sweden, not from France: the Nobel prize for Physics, awarded to the Curies and Henri Becquerel for the discovery of radioactivity. The most distinguished award which can be made to a scientist was overwhelmingly helpful in paying the overdue grocery bills.

Marie Curie regarded unemotionally, as the logical results of the original discovery, the advances which she and her fellow physicists continued to make. But early in its career, radium had given evidence of one particular property about which it was impossible to be objective. The new element had a practical as well as a theoretical value. It had become a powerful weapon in the battle against a vicious enemy.

One day early in 1901, Henri Becquerel, the old friend who had started the Curies on their world-shaking journey, appeared in the shed, smiling ruefully. "I love it," he said, "but I owe it a grudge." He was brandishing a glass tube containing a minute amount of a radium salt with which he had been experimenting.

"Sometimes I think we all owe it a grudge, and today I certainly don't love it," Marie said, looking up from the notebook in which she was recording a day's uninspired work. "What's it done?"

"It burned me," the old man announced with some pride.

The burn, he explained, was the result of a curious

accident. He had been carrying the tube in his pocket for safe keeping, and now, by a coincidence too odd to be mere chance, he had a raw welt on the skin directly beneath the pocket.

Yes, Pierre told him, radium *did* have a strange effect on the skin. He showed the old man his hands. The tips of his fingers were red and inflamed. "Now," he said to Marie, "we shall find out something more about these burns."

He bandaged a small quantity of radium on his arm. For two weeks nothing happened. Then the area covered by the radium became red and blistered. Thirty days after, there was a deep wound on the arm which did not heal for months. Yet the "burning" which had brought about this destruction of tissue had been painless. Impressed by this new manifestation, the Curies consulted with two physicians who immediately began experiments on the physiological effects of radium. The results were such as the discoverers of the element had never imagined possible.

Radium—incredible stuff—was found to have a selective action against diseased cells. When it was applied for short periods, it did no harm to healthy tissue but somehow (the exact mechanism remains doubtful), sometimes it cured cancer, the incurable. This is the property which makes it the most valuable substance in the world.

Once the facts were established, extraction of radium on a gigantic scale was begun. A commercial venture used the methods which Madame Curie had devised with an iron cauldron in the courtyard near a shack. The pure product, during the first years of its industrial life, was valued at $150,000 a gram. It is still an expensive item on any hospital budget, but after all, 1690 years will pass before a given amount loses half its weight.

The technical advice requested from the Curies by the manufacturers was granted free of charge. Marie, faced with the decision of putting a patent on her method of extraction, had said sharply, "Radium is an element. It is for everybody."

On April 19, 1906, Pierre Curie was killed in a street accident, and life as she had known it was over for Marie. The rest of it was anti-climactic—even the rewards which were her due as a scientist: the laboratory for which she had been waiting so long; her appointment to the faculty of the Sorbonne as the first woman ever to teach in the University of Paris; the second Nobel Prize, which was awarded to her in 1911 and which made her the first and only scientist who has received the honor twice.

While physicists furrowed their brows over the problems of disintegration rates, medical researchers pondered the mysteries of radium in its relation to cancer. There was much trial and error during the early days; there remains much speculation on the exact nature of the phenomenon. But the question of how and when to use radium was eventually worked out down to the smallest detail. The X-ray, as is predictable from its identification with the gamma-ray of radium, was soon found to have a similar effect on the human body. It is a less expensive, more easily available method of treatment, although in some cases—in most cancers of the skin and in cancer of the cervix—radium is distinctly preferable to the X-ray.

Cancer itself remains the most destructive disease in the world. "It is only fair to note parenthetically," remarked the late Dr. Logan Clendening in *The Human Body*, "that while no positive results have been obtained along any line, it is not for want of trying. Experimental cancer research is being carried on all over the world by groups of the most honest-minded and indefatigable investigators the ranks of science can command. The problem has been attacked by every known method in the armamentarium of science. It has been attacked with the weapons of bacteriology, of immunity, of biological chemistry, of physics, of physical chemistry, of tissue pathology, of genetics, of heredity, of animal experimentation, and of cytology. Those smug people who are wont to say, 'Now it is time some of you medical men should get to work and find the cause of cancer,' are simply pathetically ignorant. We seem to have arrived at an impasse. We are in much the same position as the students of infectious diseases before Pasteur. When the key to the nature of neoplasms is found, if ever it is, it will probably be as new an idea as Pasteur's idea of germs.

And just as Pasteur's work opened up totally new fields, such as surgery and immunology, so this discovery will probably be felt in dark and obscure corners of human ignorance."

Those words were written over twenty years ago. There is even now little to add to them. And today, at the half-century mark, radium and the X-ray remain the only nonsurgical treatments known for cancer. Whatever we will find out some day about cancer, the discovery of the therapeutic use of these two agents is a milestone along the weary road. It is up to the scientists of the future to find the end of the road.

part II

The Druggist and the Doctor

3

The Drug Industry Grows

HERR CRAMER said sternly, "It's better to get the shop closed on time tonight, Friederich, than to bother me with so many questions."

He was a mild-natured man, was Herr Cramer, but occasionally the conversation of his moody apprentice irritated him. Young Sertürner was a good boy, the old man thought sadly. If he worked hard enough, he might even make a good pharmacist some day. Too bad he was always fretting about things that did not concern him. Herr Cramer then felt a twinge of conscience and added kindly, "We've been through it before, remember, Friederich? Last night? And the night before? What I told you then is still true. There's nothing anybody can do about opium. We have to take it as we find it. Or," he added, grumbling, "leave it alone altogether. That's the best idea."

"But Herr Cramer!" The apprentice leaned his broom against the counter and went into the back room of the shop, from which his master had been lecturing him. "Isn't it true that opium is the only drug in the world that relieves pain?"

Herr Cramer nodded. "*Ja,* but——"

"And isn't it true that some doctors won't even use it because they never know exactly what it will do?"

Herr Cramer nodded, "*Ja,* but——"

"But isn't it true that the exact same dose—the *exact* same, mind you—can kill one man and not even make another sleepy?"

Herr Cramer grew tired of nodding and agreeing. He stood up and said testily, "So for"—he tried a rapid mental calculation and failed—"maybe 5000 years doctors have been using opium, good or bad." He advanced two steps toward the boy and added with some asperity, "And all of a sudden, in 1803, Friederich Wilhelm Sertürner of Paderborn is going to make opium work on schedule. I don't know what's happened to young people today. When I was a boy I didn't think I knew twice as much as the rest of the world put together . . . And don't forget to dust the scales before you go!"

"Not *make* opium work on schedule," Friederich

said, choosing to ignore the last remark. "Find out why it works some of the time and then——"

"*Ach, mein Gott!*" the old man said, stamping out of the shop. "Always this Friederich must have the last word." But he shouted back, "Don't be late closing up. Your mama gets worried about you!" She had good cause, he thought. He himself would not care to bring up such a son.

Left alone, Friederich returned to the front of the shop, picked up his broom, and considered the tasks which faced him. He had to dust the scales, sweep the shop, replace all the bottles on their proper shelves, repair the broken filter, fill three prescriptions–long ones–to be picked up first thing in the morning, make a fresh batch of——

Suddenly he said to himself, "Why don't I just try it?" He threw his broom to the floor and walked into the back room. The jar stood on the topmost shelf. He set it on the table, opened it, and prodded the gummy mass of opium gently.

"For maybe 5000 years, doctors have been using opium, good or bad, and all of a sudden, in 1803 Friederich Wilhelm Sertürner of Paderborn is going to make it work on schedule!"

Cramer's words, foolish as the apprentice considered them, had remained with Sertürner. He looked at the mass in front of him and sighed. The clock in the tower of the city hall began to strike nine. He should get his work done, he thought. He really should. . . .

As a matter of historical fact, there was nothing foolish in Herr Cramer's comments. Opium had been in use for well over 5000 years; it had passed from Sumerians to Egyptians to Arabians, then been adopted by Venetians, Portuguese, Dutchmen, and in time, by all Europeans. Paracelsus, the pioneer of modern chemists, whose office was in whatever place he stopped his horse, had always carried opium with him in the pommel of his saddle. "The stone of immortality," he called it. Paracelsus dissolved the gummy substance in alcohol, forming laudanum, and for years that was the standard form in which the drug was dispensed.

But early in the eighteenth century a doctor popularized an opium mixture of such ferocity that shortly thereafter the drug fell into disrepute, and its use in any form or quantity was almost negligible by the time Sertürner began his experiments. It all came about through a bizarre set of circumstances.

Thomas Dover was captain of a small privateer called the *Duke,* which set sail in 1710 from the island of Juan Fernandez, bound for England. One of the men aboard his ship was Alexander Selkirk, who made himself famous by telling the story of his adventures on Juan Fernandez to a journalist named Daniel Defoe. The result was *Robinson Crusoe.*

Dover was a dark, evil-faced adventurer, who had surprising aspirations. Piracy was profitable enough, but he wanted to be a doctor. He fulfilled this wish by the simple expedient of sending around notices that he was available for consultation. He looked with scorn on half-hearted methods and timid doses, for he himself operated on the theory that if one grain of a drug is good, then three grains must be three times as good. His staggering prescriptions became alarmingly popular.

Early in his medical career Dover developed a favorite gout remedy—a blend of opium and ipecac which, with characteristic modesty, he called "Dover's powder." He dispensed the remedy in doses of 60 to 100 grains, quantities to make his present-day colleagues blanch and reach for a stomach pump. (Five to ten grains is the standard dosage in the U. S. Pharmacopeia, which continues to list the *pulvis ipecacuanhae et opii* as an historical curiosity.) Dover had a wide influence and a bad reputation. Dover's powder, and thus opium in any form, developed the same reputation. The rising generation of doctors was taught to administer laudanum sparingly, although it was the only agent then known which could combat the pain of disease. Organized medicine concluded sadly that since pain was the natural fruit of man's evil nature, nothing could be done about it. This was still the situation in 1803.

Sertürner shook some opium out of the jar and looked at it searchingly. "It stands to reason," he said aloud (he often held involved conversations with himself) "that if opium works some of the time, it should work *all* the time. There's nothing wrong with the drug. It's the doctors' fault. They just don't know how to regulate the dose." Like most apothecaries of the day young Sertürner had no use for doctors, but it occurred to him that in this case they must be given some small benefit of doubt. "They don't know how to regulate the dose," he repeated, this time adding, "*Why* don't they know?" Sertürner leaned an elbow on the table and frowned moodily at the opium jar.

The same dose, he thought, can kill one man but not even make another man sleepy.

"The same drug," he said aloud. "It works some of the time—but not all of the time."

It was then that an idea came to the pharmacist's apprentice, a critical idea which had not occurred to the wise men of medicine in all the centuries opium had been used. Perhaps hidden away in the mass of gum, powder, and resin there was an essential substance which caused the characteristic effects of opium. But perhaps this unknown was temperamental enough to distribute itself unevenly throughout the material in which it was hidden. In that case there would be no way of knowing how much of the active ingredient was present in a given amount, which might explain why the same dose of opium could be either ineffective or deadly. Now if one could isolate this active ingredient . . .

He put a few ounces of opium into a beaker and wondered what to do with it. Water, presumably, was a good starting point. He poured some over the opium. He could see that something had dissolved. It was not much of a beginning, he thought.

It was, in fact, only the beginning of months and months and more months of work: unpromising work done after hours in the darkened shop, or squeezed in between chores and customers; work abandoned frequently in despair, taken up again with enthusiasm at the approach of a new idea, based more on hunches than on carefully plotted procedure. Sertürner could not run to the library for answers to his questions. There were no answers, because no one before him had ever even thought of the questions. He simply poured chemicals over the opium, inventing laboratory techniques as he went along.

One day, for no particular reason, he decided to dissolve some opium in acid and to neutralize the acid with ammonia. For a moment nothing happened. Then before his wide-opened eyes, a shower of gleaming white crystals formed around the sides of the tube and began to settle to the bottom. This was a tangible result, even though he was not sure what the crystals were.

"There's one way to find out," he thought.

Cramer's pharmacy had rats, as did all pharmacies. They were Sertürner's nocturnal companions. He had long ago grown used to seeing their eyes glitter out of the dark corners of the room as he worked through the night. He caught two of the fattest among them. To one he fed the brown, bitter solid from which the shining crystals had separated.

Nothing happened.

To the other he fed the crystals themselves, sprinkled on a piece of stale bread.

The rat slept—for nearly two days—revived, ate some more crystals, slept again, then gave up and died. The age-old secret of the poppy had been brought to light by a twenty-three-year-old apprentice druggist with a few drops of household ammonia.

For three years he went over the same ground, ferreting out the best way to extract the pure "somniferous principle" from its camouflage. He perfected his method, dissolving and redissolving the crystals in acid, ether, alcohol, anything that would dissolve them, until only about twelve percent of the original weight of the opium remained. The twelve percent, he decided, represented absolutely pure crystals. He delved into their chemistry, discovering to his vast satisfaction that they were alkaline. They turned red litmus paper blue; they neutralized acid. The textbooks which said that plant derivatives contained no alkalis were wrong. Textbooks, it seemed, could be wrong about a lot of things.

In 1806, Sertürner published the results of those historic "fifty-seven experiments." It was the official statement of the discovery: Herr Sertürner of Paderborn had extracted the active principle of opium. The paper did not say that Herr Sertürner of Paderborn had also established the modern science of pharmacology. But he had.

He began to wonder exactly what practical value was in his fifty-seven experiments. He had moved to the Hanoverian city of Einbeck. He had his own pharmacy now. He was a highly respected citizen. People trusted him, even when he came to them asking mysterious favors. One day he called on an acquaintance and said:

"Ludwig, if you're game for a little scientific experiment, come by the shop tonight at ten o'clock."

He rounded up three young men who were game for anything. They assembled after his closing hour and soon found themselves seated at the table in Sertürner's back room, solemnly eating the crystals which he handed out to them and to himself, a half-grain at a time. They sat for a few moments in silence, each watching the faces of the other three growing flushed and feverish, each wondering how his own face was reacting. Then, in quavering voices, the three visitors recited their symptoms for Sertürner, while he made straggling entries into his notebook. "After half a grain, increased bodily activity, redness of face . . . after the second half-grain, slight nausea, dullness of mind, numbness . . ." They were having difficulty articulating now. Sertürner found it almost impossible to write. Before his hand lost all control, he scrawled the information that an aching tooth did not hurt him any more. He pushed the third half-grain toward his friends. Their heads were sinking onto the table. They tried to stretch out their hands toward the last dose and failed. Sertürner made a heroic effort to escape from the world of dreams into which he was sinking, and swallowed another half-grain. Before he fell asleep he was aware of being so depressed that his last conscious thought was a profound wish never to wake up.

He woke up, hours later, so ill that he was sorry that his wish had not been granted. He did not realize how close it had come to being fulfilled. With some difficulty he aroused his companions. As soon as they could move, the three young men staggered out of the shop into a dawn as gloomy as their dispositions. If they never saw him again, they told Sertürner, they would consider themselves lucky. He had poisoned them, they said. He had done exactly that. Each of them had consumed more than three times the safe maximum dose.

But to Sertürner the distress of his stomach and his friends was of great profit. Having found out how much of the stuff *not* to give was, in its fashion, an accomplishment. The following night, alone this time, he began again, understandably working with smaller doses. When he had taken about a quarter of a grain, he lay down and went to sleep. There was no nausea or depression now. There were only dreams that he left behind with regret. When he was fully awake it came to him that the somniferous principle of opium deserved a name of its own. He would name it after Morpheus, the god of sleep.

He called it morphia, a poetic form later given a good chemical ending in "ine."

When Sertürner published a paper on the physical effects of morphine and the now fool-proof method of regulating the dose, it was received at first with acclaim. The more perceptive members of the medical profession realized well enough what had happened. Not only had the first great step been taken in solving the problem of pain, but a new field of research had been opened. Sertürner was feted from Lisbon to St. Petersburg. Seven universities awarded him honorary degrees. The French Academy of Science, always practical, awarded him a two-thousand-franc prize that carried with it the awesome title, "Benefactor of Mankind."

This was the first reaction. Soon after it came a reversal of feeling. Goaded by professional jealousy and the overpowering fear of change in the established order, the academic gossips went to work. Slanderous reports, first about his work, then about the man himself, began to circulate. Herr Sertürner, the professors said, might fool the ignorant with his shockingly unscientific carryings-on, but surely he did not expect *them* to be taken in. Opium was poison. It had always been poison. If some druggist or other thought that by adding a few chemicals to it or by giving it a mythological name he could make opium anything but a poison, he had better think again. Extracting the active principle of a medicinal plant—ridiculous!

In no time at all the dispute became one of personalities, picked up with enthusiasm by the tea-party gossips as well as the jealous academicians. The man was a fraud, the people of Einbeck decided, and he was the least respectable sort of fraud they could imagine. If black magic were to be worked with opium, the devil's weed, let it be worked elsewhere than in the pharmacy of Einbeck. The wrath of the good citizens became so violent that at last Sertürner grew sick at heart and abandoned his home and then his work.

He took refuge in Hamelin, city of the Pied Piper. His powers of research were then turned to a problem of pure chemistry in no way related to medicine. He became an expert on explosives and fire-arms manufacture, producing a new alloy of lead and antimony which proved to be as deadly a gunpowder as was then in existence. And for these activities he was highly respected by the people of Hamelin.

This was a tragic paradox, but not so tragic as that which marked the unhappy last years of his life. During a long, painful illness, his stomach was so affected that he could retain neither food nor medicine. Sertürner had given mankind the power to reduce pain and to die in peace, but it was of no help to him in his mortal agony. He died late in February of 1841.

If only Sertürner had been able to see into the future, he might have felt that his achievement compensated in some measure for the suffering it had cost him. But it would have been almost impossible for anyone in 1841 to comprehend the future of the science which Sertürner had given a system.

The drug counter in the corner drugstore is a comfortable commonplace in our lives. We rarely wonder what procedures are set in motion when we bring in the doctor's familiar (usually illegible!) prescription labeled ℞, which is an abbreviation of the Latin *recipe*—take. Take what? The doctor has a choice of any one of the thousands of drugs to be found in the United States Pharmacopeia. His prescription may thus be adapted to an almost infinite variety of complaints, and when the prescription is filled, the patient will swallow pills or capsules or a liquid containing drugs which are pure, carefully tested, and rigidly standardized. To the science of pharmacology as we know it today, many men have made contributions. Most of them have drawn on principles that were established in the back room of Cramer's pharmacy.

Although Sertürner's work was ignored by many of his contemporaries, it made a vigorous impression on a young Frenchman named Pierre Pelletier, a chemist and professor of pharmacy. Pelletier became obsessed with a theory which Sertürner's papers suggested to him. Surely, he thought, the poppy was not so different from other plants. Could it be that every medicinal plant in use concealed its essential material in a confusion of useless gum, oil, and resin? The idea was enough to make a sensitive chemist dizzy.

Pelletier joined forces with a friend, a retail pharmacist named Caventou, and together they went to work. With scientific training and technical skill which would have made poor Sertürner frantic with jealousy, the two proceeded to isolate a great many pure chemicals in the plant kingdom. In the poisonous strychnos plant they found pure strychnine; in ipecac, emetine; in angostura bark, brucine; in sabadilla seeds, veratrine; in pepper, piperine; in the delphinium plant, delphinine. Other scientists, spurred on by the example of the two Frenchmen, joined in the great "active principle" hunt. Tobacco leaves yielded nicotine; belladonna leaves atropine. All over Europe chemists were hard at work pulling apart leaves and roots and barks.

All these discoveries were important in principle, but Pelletier was essentially a practical man. "As a chemist," he announced tartly one day, "I'm delighted to know that the strychnos plant contains a pure chemical named strychnine. That's just fine. But as a pharmacist, I'm unimpressed."

Caventou nodded sagely, neglecting to point out that he, as a retail pharmacist instead of an academician, was even less impressed. "Now," Pelletier went on heatedly, "since we seem to have a talent for finding hidden chemicals, can't we do something more for the human race than find new ways to poison it?"

"It seems reasonable," Caventou agreed. "Where were you thinking of looking?"

"For an 'active principle' to set Europe back on its heels?" Pelletier said, smiling. "That's easy." And then, not without a faint sense of trepidation, he cleared his laboratory for a series of new experiments.

In the far-distant jungles of South America grew a mysterious tree which the Indians called the *quinaquina.* No one knew how or why it operated, but because of it, an undeterminable number of people were saved from death caused by a vicious disease. Malaria had been known for centuries before anyone had ever heard of *quinaquina* bark. Anyone, that is, except the Indians of Peru. The bark was their discovery and might have remained their possession if no less eminent a lady than the Countess of Chinchón had not come down with malaria. Other people who had malaria simply shivered and rattled their teeth until they recovered or died. But the Countess? The wife of Don Luis Geronimo Fernandez de Cabrero de Bobadilla y Mendoza, fourth Count of Chinchón, Viceroy of Peru, member of a family who had the inherited privilege of remaining seated and even hatted in the presence of the King of Spain? When the Countess took to her bed shaking, all Peru shook with her. Since there was no effective remedy for the disease, and since the Countess was a delicate lady who could not depend on her constitution to pull her through, she was given up for lost. The governor of an obscure Peruvian province journeyed all the way to the capital to talk the Countess's physicians into trying the old Indian remedy for malaria, since all else had failed . . . All else *had* failed. The *quinaquina* bark did not. Within a week after her first taste of the bitter brew, the Countess, to the amazement of her doctor and her husband, was out of danger.

This was the story, at any rate, and although it was never fully authenticated, it was an extremely popular tale which brought the Peruvian bark into Europe under favorable auspices. For two hundred years cinchona bark, as it was eventually christened in honor of the Countess, amassed a dazzling history compounded partly of romantic legends and partly of the cold-blooded facts of finance and trade monopoly. In any case, in the pharmacopeia of 1817 there was no drug more prominent than cinchona. Nor was there any drug which was less understood by chemists. Pierre Pelletier, seeking more significant research than finding the active ingredient in pepper, did not have far to look.

Other chemists had played about with the cinchona bark, as Pelletier well knew. They had found a number of chemicals in it, but no one constituent which cured malaria. Pelletier, however, with Sertürner in mind, had a lead which the others had overlooked. He had a hunch that he was looking for an alkaloid, and he proceeded accordingly, working on both gray and yellow varieties of cinchona bark.

He extracted two chemical curiosities, one from each type of bark. In the gray bark he found white crystals—beautiful, shining white slivers which turned red litmus blue and neutralized acid. They were a chemist's dream of an alkaloid compound. The yellow bark produced a rather messy looking gum which refused to crystallize and which could be dissolved in practically anything. It was unattractive, but it was certainly a brand-new chemical. Pelletier's work was temporarily over. From here on, he wrote, it was up to the physicians. As a chemist he could isolate new chemicals, but he could not test them on patients.

He had plenty of cooperation. Cinchona and anything connected with cinchona were highly thought of. The new products were tested on a number of malaria cases and the results were reported back to Pelletier. The beautiful white crystals might have been table salt for all the effect they had on the disease; the messy yellow gum cured every case in which it was tried. It was the active principle of cinchona, the first pure chemical in history to cure a specific disease. Pelletier called it quinine, after a Peruvian word meaning bark. The science of pharmacology had advanced another hundred years.

Pelletier's discovery had repercussions in all the laboratories of Europe. Announcements of new medical compounds came so quickly that the doctors could hardly keep up with the chemists. What the doctors did not realize was that they had not even begun to explore the possibilities of chemicals in conquering disease.

Breaking down a natural compound into its component parts was all well enough, but there was another idea which soon made an irresistible appeal to the ambitious chemists. No longer did they consider themselves mere investigators of matter as nature presented it to them. Nature was lavish, but not always thorough. Suppose that in some cases she had provided the component parts of a drug, but had neglected to put them together? In such a case man could improve on her and produce a needed compound.

No sooner had Pelletier succeeded in isolating pure quinine than a feverish attempt began in laboratories all over the world to synthesize the wonder drug. This was unsuccessful until 1944, over one hundred years later. In 1856, however, a colorful dye was produced in one of the experiments intended to create quinine. It was called "Perkins' purple," a name later changed to the less descriptive but more poetic "Perkins' mauve." Dr. Perkins' discovery was the first of the coal-tar derivatives, and revolutionized the dye industry. Its appearance in a period of phenomenal advances in organic chemistry had the effect of setting a match to a firecracker.

In the field of medicine, the idea of synthesizing drugs took hold largely through a series of happy accidents. The first was Hermann Kolbe's. Kolbe was a big man in the German chemical industry, big in girth as well as reputation, feared for his caustic tongue as much as his great accomplishments. He had been the first chemist to synthesize an organic compound—acetic acid—from the raw materials of nature. Dr. Kolbe was currently interested in carbolic acid, the reeking antiseptic which an English surgeon named Joseph Lister had established in every operating room. Carbolic acid, or phenol, was a germicide. It was also a poison. One could spray it on a patient's wounds to protect him from external infections; one could hardly force it down his throat to cure him of internal ones.

Nearly twenty years before, however, Kolbe had found that he could convert phenol into another kind of acid called salicylic. In 1875, when Mr. Lister's curious habit of washing surgical instruments in carbolic acid had become widespread, Kolbe remembered that little chemical exercise. Salicylic acid had two qualities which endeared it to his professional heart. It was nonpoisonous, and it broke down in the test-tube to form carbolic acid once again. If salicylic acid would undergo the same breaking-down process in the body—and why shouldn't it?—the results might be very interesting.

Salicylic acid, he found in short order, worked laboratory miracles. It preserved milk; it prevented meat from decaying. It killed microbes. Kolbe was pleased with his brain child. Eventually he allowed his medical friends to take over the experiments, and in no time at all salicylic acid was famous, its praises sung from one end of Europe to the other. It was far superior to the old reeking carbolic, the doctors said. It did not irritate wounds. It healed them. And when a patient drank it, it made him feel so much better. Salicylic acid was undoubtedly the greatest chemical of its day.

For a year or so these optimistic reports poured in. Then the doctors began to notice something strange. Salicylic acid undoubtedly made their patients *feel* better, but it didn't really cure them of anything. There were still people who died of pneumonia and typhoid, and people who got better. The rate of recovery was the same as it had always been. Doctors began to have the uneasy feeling that salicylic acid had nothing to do with it.

Gradually the facts forced their way to the surface. Salicylic acid, once taken internally, had no connection whatsoever with carbolic acid. What exactly could it do? No one was quite sure any more.

It was Dr. Carl Emil Buss who figured it out. His patients drank salicylic acid, as did everyone else's patients. And some of them died, just like other doctors' patients. Then why, Dr. Buss asked himself, did this salicylic acid make them feel, look, and act as though they were going to live? Dr. Buss thought and observed and experimented, and finally came up with the answer. His patients felt better because in every case their fever—no matter what its cause—was temporarily reduced by the acid.

The idea astounded him. Salicylic acid was supposed to be a germ-killer, not a fever-reducer. Quinine was the fever-reducer. Salicylic acid was supposed to destroy germs, not bring relief from pain. Morphine was the pain-killer.

Dr. Buss and the thousands of doctors who read his historic report immediately realized its significance. Here was an agent far cheaper than quinine and far safer than morphine. It could do the work of both in the many cases which did not require the strength of more powerful drugs.

This discovery fired the chemists with enthusiasm which they translated into fast and efficient action, producing innumerable chemical agents. In 1883 a young German chemist named Ludwig Knorr, playing with an organic chemical named quinoline, accidentally put together a compound which was later named antipyrine. No one had ever seen anything quite like this antipyrine. It was completely synthetic, its structure plotted by the chemist as an architect designs a house. It relieved the pain of rheumatism, of backaches, headaches, earaches, toothaches. It reduced all but the most stubborn fevers. It was the first important man-made drug, and its invention launched a spectacular new business—the synthetic-drug industry.

The full history of the industry, of course, will not be written and should not be predicted for many years to come. Considering that it came into prominence late in the last century and has, by the first half of this one, produced such chemical triumphs as the sulfa family, we may at least venture the opinion that it is off to a good start.

Few industries have managed to produce their most widely used products as quickly as the synthetic drug industry. Professional jealousy was behind the accomplishment. The success of antipyrine set every industrial chemist in Germany on the trail of a rival product. In rapid sequence a number of improved fever-fighters, some with names that are still familiar, were produced.

In 1899, officials at the great Friederich Bayer dye works began to worry because other concerns were producing fast-selling remedies more rapidly than most people could learn to spell "phenacetin." The Bayer Company, its officials decided, would get down to work and bring out one great drug which would put all others in the shade.

Bayer's star chemist, Felix Hoffman, went to work on the problem. He attacked it with true Teutonic thoroughness. "What is the original and the most effective of these fever remedies?" he asked himself. Salicylic acid. Why were the later inventions considered superior to it? Simply because they were less irritating to the stomach. All he had to do, then, was to find something with all the advantages of salicylic acid but none of the disadvantages. He began a systematic study of every known compound of salicylic acid. Years before, a now-forgotten chemist had produced a derivative of the acid which attached a collection of atoms called the "acetate" group to the molecule of the acid. The result was a chemical curiosity which had no application at the time. Hoffman, however, found out one day that there was in existence a product called acetyl-salicylic acid. In the course of his research, he put a note on the agenda of the Bayer medical department saying, "Try this out."

The results could not have failed to please the most pessimistic holder of Bayer stock. From hospitals and from private practices came word the company had been waiting for. Acetyl-salicylic acid was undoubtedly the most effective, yet mildest, fever-reducer and pain-reliever ever produced. Once on the market, it would undoubtedly dwarf all other synthetic drugs.

For what was about to be the most popular drug on the shelf, a new name was required. After all, one could not expect people to go into a pharmacy and ask for a bottle of acetyl-salicylic acid pills. Could they drop a few letters here and there and call the products a-salicin or a-salicylic? No. It would be better to get away from the word "salicylic" altogether. Their drug must not be confused with anything old and inferior . . . Perhaps there was a suggestion in some other field. The chemical had been produced synthetically since 1856, but it did occur in nature in the oil of the spiraea leaf. Acetyl-spiraea? Acetyl-spirin? That would do very nicely, if only it were a little shorter. They might drop all or part of the "acetyl."

They settled on "aspirin."

4

Vitamins

ON August 13, 1768, a reconverted freighter in the service of his Britannic Majesty, George III, sailed out of Plymouth to look for a new continent and to find the distance between the sun and the earth. Such, in any case, were the respective intentions of the British Admiralty and the British Royal Society for the Improvement of Natural Knowledge.

The Royal Society's interest in that ambitious cruise was the direct result of a prediction made by Edmund Halley, of comet fame. "In June of 1769," the court astronomer said, "the planet Venus will pass directly between the sun and the earth and show itself clearly on the sun's disc."

"If the transit of Venus is observed from various points on the earth's surface," said the president of the

Royal Society with more optimism than accuracy, "then we can finally determine the distance between the sun and the earth."

"If we fit up a ship to land the Royal Society men on Tahiti to watch their confounded eclipse," inquired the British Admiralty, "what's to prevent the captain of the ship from looking for the Southern Continent on his way home?"

The Southern Continent! The British Admiralty yearned after that great, rich, temperate land. To annex so wealthy a possession, every monarch in Europe would have given half his possessions. No country had yet found and laid claim to it. One obstacle lay in the way of discovery.

There *was* no Southern Continent. It was a dream world, no less illusory than a Gulliver-traveled land, but attested to by some of the most technical and authoritative documents in the annals of navigation.

The ship chosen for the dual task of finding the Southern Continent and determining the astronomic mileage was a dumpy vessel called the *Endeavour*. On its preparation for the three-year voyage, the Admiralty officials spent exactly 5,394 pounds, 15 shillings and 4 pence. And to command it they appointed a hard-boiled Yorkshireman named James Cook.

It must be understood that so far as the Admiralty and the Royal Society were concerned, the cruise of the *Endeavour* was not a success. The value of the transit observations fell far short of the Society's expectations; the Southern Continent remained undiscovered. Yet in spite of this record of total failure, the cruise of the *Endeavour* became one of the greatest in history, owing to the fact that James Cook was an extraordinarily stubborn fellow.

It was because of vitamins, of all things.

James Cook, of course, would go to his grave without ever knowing what a vitamin was, and having no suspicion that such a thing existed. His interest in nutrition stemmed from the practical desire to sail to Tahiti and back without losing three-quarters of his crew to scurvy.

The real scourge of the eighteenth-century seafarer was not so exciting as pirates, nor so dignified as hidden reefs, shifting currents, and changing winds. These were occupational hazards, but with a little luck one could evade them. Scurvy was the problem that never failed to arise; it was the nightmare of every sea captain who contemplated a voyage over three months long.

The symptoms were unmistakable: the gums bled; the teeth became loose, then fell out; other parts of the body began rotting away; the ankles swelled; internal hemorrhages began and continued until delirium and death ended the agony.

Lieutenant Cook considered the three years' voyage ahead and wondered what could be done. During his twenty years of service he had acquired a number of surprising ideas about the proper management of a ship, two of which were shockingly radical. He believed that the sailors should live in clean, well-ventilated quarters instead of in the filthy holes which were usually reserved for them, and that their standard diet of salted beef and suet pudding should be revised to include fresh fruits and vegetables.

This idea had not originated with Cook. One hundred and fifty-one years before the cruise of the *Endeavour* a surgeon named Woodall, employed by the East India Company, had written a little book called *The Surgeon's Mate,* a handbook of practical suggestions for the ship's doctor. In it he stated clearly that lemon juice is of great value in the prevention of scurvy. It was a Navy surgeon named James Lind who brought Woodall's advice to the attention of the eighteenth century. In his *Treatise on Scurvy,* which appeared in 1754, he described an experiment which he performed on twelve scurvy patients. Two he treated with oranges and lemons; the rest with strong and mild acids, sea water, and nutmeg. Of this strange pharmacopeia, Lind says: "The consequence was that the most sudden and visible good effects were perceived from the use of the oranges and lemons; one of those who had taken them being at the end of six days fit for duty." Good as Lind's evidence was, no sea captain, until 1768, ever put his idea to a large-scale test.

Lind and Cook both had the incorrect notion that

dampness and dirt were as much responsible for scurvy as lack of fresh food. It was a happy mistake on their part, for it improved the hygienic conditions on board ship as nothing but fear of the disease could have done.

Now Lieutenant Cook prepared his supplies. Into the galley of the *Endeavour* poured such foodstuffs as the ship's cook had never before seen at sea. The Captain's plans seemed designed to include refuelling stops at almost every island between England and Tahiti.

Seven and one-half months after the *Endeavour* left Plymouth, she reached the island of Tahiti. There was not one case of scurvy aboard.

The transit of Venus was observed by the Royal Society's representatives and recorded on canvas by the official artist of the expedition as the ship lay at anchor in Matavai Bay. After three months they proceeded to other matters of interest to the Crown. Cook explored New Zealand and became the first European to set foot on its shore; he surveyed the entire east coast of Australia, claiming the southeast sector of the continent and naming it New South Wales. In October of 1770, a few days out of Java, he wrote: "I have the satisfaction to say that I have not lost one man by sickness during the whole voyage," thus stating casually a fact of great significance for all future maritime history. His satisfaction, unfortunately, was premature. The crew of the *Endeavour*, after sailing in roaring good health through the primitive islands of the Pacific, was stricken almost immediately when the ship anchored at Batavia, Java, the first "civilized" city seen in three years. "We came here with as healthy a ship's company as need go to sea," Cook said, "and after a stay of not quite three months left in the condition of a hospital ship, besides the loss of seven men." Most of these deaths were the result of the terrible jungle fevers which prevailed on the island.

The British Admiralty was more interested in Cook's charts of the Pacific than in the daily diet of his crew. Not until the conclusion of his second great voyage of exploration did Cook begin to press his ideas. In 1775 he read a paper before the Royal Society, "On the Prevention of Scurvy at Sea." It is a classic in medical and maritime history. Compulsory rations of lemon and lime juice became such a characteristic feature of the British Navy that British sailors soon were nicknamed "Limeys." To all practical purposes, scurvy ceased to be a problem on land as well as on sea by 1800. Rarely has any disease been so easily overcome.

The conquest of scurvy was empiric—a triumph of pure observation and experience. Not for another hundred years would anyone begin to understand why fresh fruits and vegetables both prevented and cured the disease.

The first clue came in 1886, in that same town of Batavia which had once changed the luck of the *Endeavour*. Scurvy was not involved, nor had it ever occurred to anyone that beriberi, a vicious Oriental disease, had the remotest relation to it. On the surface there seems little connection between the crew of the good ship *Endeavour* and the chickens dying in the back yard of a Batavia military hospital.

But there is.

The military hospital of Batavia had a new director, a tough, no-nonsense-about-this-now sort of officer. Like most newly appointed military men, the official brought to his job the conviction that his predecessors had been very lax. It was during the earliest days of his tenure of office that he found out about Dr. Eijkman's chickens.

The doctor himself was one of a commission appointed by the Dutch government to investigate beriberi. The Singhalese word from which beriberi is derived means "great weakness." The disease was aptly named. A beriberi victim had swollen arms and legs which were crippled by neuritis. A characteristic "beriberi heart" was revealed at whatever few autopsies were done on persons who had died of a disease that could be recognized so easily.

Medical opinion on beriberi was divided. Causes ranging from arsenical poisoning to bad housing were variously suggested. But by 1886 the "germ theory" of disease was so universally accepted that any illness of unknown origin was assumed to be caused by a microbe. The Dutch commission in Batavia took up its work with the idea that beriberi was an infectious disease. After a few months of unsatisfactory investigations, it reported that it could not find the germ of the sickness, and went home. Only Dr. Christiaan Eijkman, dissatisfied with the work the commission had done, stayed on in Java, determined to find the new microbe.

He was made the laboratory director of the Batavia Hospital. While the new superintendent's appointment was being processed, Dr. Eijkman was hot on the trail of the beriberi microbe. Cultures from every beriberi patient in the hospital filled his laboratory; slide after slide passed across the stage of his microscope. Eijkman was not discouraged when he found no trace of a characteristic microbe. His master, Koch, had looked at slides for half a year before he had seen the first tuberculosis bacillus. Patience was standard equipment for a bacteriologist.

Eijkman had a number of experimental fowls which he hoped to infect with the disease by injecting them with supposedly virulent matter from beriberi victims. The fowls, in the face of all his effort, stubbornly remained healthy. Puzzled, Eijkman decided that the birds were immune to the disease. He abandoned this line of investigation and moved his chickens into the back yard of the hospital, leaving orders for them to be fed on scraps from the hospital kitchen. The birds now began living on the unvaried diet of every native on the island—rice and more rice.

Eijkman forgot about them. Then one day a soldier,

into whose custody the fowls had temporarily fallen, stopped by the laboratory and said, "Doctor, don't you want to get rid of those chickens?"

Eijkman looked up from his microscope and stared in amazement. "Get rid of the chickens? Why? I might want to use them again, if——"

"Better hurry, then, Doctor. Those birds have only a few more days on earth. Must be discouraging to the patients to look out the window and see 'em."

Eijkman realized that he had neither seen the chickens nor thought about them for almost two weeks. He shrugged, mildly irritated. "What happened to them? Were they starved?"

"Starved! They've been eating just what the patients eat. I don't know what's wrong with 'em, but they sure look sad."

Curious, Eijkman went down to the kitchen garden and cast a professional eye over his fowls. They looked sad indeed. Their feathers drooped; their heads hung at a strange angle; their legs wobbled. Eijkman had seen the symptoms before, too many times not to recognize them now.

"See, Doc?" the attendant said. "Shall I get rid of them, or——?"

"No! They're more valuable now than they ever were."

"Wh——?"

"They have beriberi!"

The soldier sighed patiently. "So has every other

native in Java. I never thought it was the thing to look for in chickens."

"But now I have an experimental animal to work with!"

Eijkman hurried back to his laboratory without further conversation. He had experimental animals. But he had something more important, too. He had a logical new theory about the cause of beriberi. The chickens had been healthy eating poultry feed in his laboratory. Fed on rice in the yard, they developed beriberi. The entire population of the island ate rice, too. It seemed a safe enough bet that the beriberi germ made its home in the rice grain. In any case, Eijkman thought as he walked back jubilantly, now that he knew where to look for it, he would track it down in short order.

At the time Dr. Eijkman planned his campaign, the new superintendent of the hospital was busy mapping out strategy for cutting down the hospital budget. The kitchen was the obvious starting point. One can imagine him stalking about, his lips pursed thoughtfully, while the unnerved staff answered his questions. Until finally. . . .

"You there! Where are you taking that rice?"

"To the chickens, sir."

"Chickens? What chickens?"

"Dr. Eijkman's chickens, sir."

"*Chickens!*"

Memorandum to Dr. Eijkman: "Kindly report to

the office of the superintendent at your earliest convenience."

"Now see here, Doctor, what's all this about your birds eating food from the hospital kitchen?"

"Scraps, sir. They——"

"Scraps? Scraps aren't food, I suppose! Eh?"

"Yes, sir. But——"

"Ah, now we're getting somewhere. They *are* eating food from the kitchen. Government supplies, eh!"

Dr. Eijkman said, "They're experimental animals, sir. They have beriberi!"

"Beriberi?" The superintendent looked suspicious. "You're supposed to be doing the laboratory work of this hospital, not undertaking research on beriberi. The government has spent enough money on that. I want this waste stopped at once. If you must feed those half-dead birds, feed 'em unhusked rice, or anything you like. But *not* hospital supplies! That's all, Doctor."

Eijkman went back to his laboratory and the chief went back to his study of the budget.

Unhappy chickens! Not even the poorest native of the most primitive village ate rice which had not been milled to remove its outer husk. It was the one small luxury in an otherwise barren existence. Still, Eijkman thought, *gaba*—unhusked rice—was about as cheap as food could be. He bought the chickens a supply of the unappealing stuff, convinced that they would not notice any appreciable difference.

The difference, as it turned out, was one that the

fowls could not help noticing. Within twenty-four hours after their harsh regimen started, they were clearly on the mend. A day later, to all appearances, they were completely recovered, their necks back at a proper angle, their once-paralyzed legs carrying them all over the yard in pursuit of food more succulent than unmilled rice.

Eijkman surveyed the barnyard scene before him with surprise. Polished rice produced beriberi? Unpolished rice cured it?

He bought some new birds and took them up to his laboratory. He divided them into two groups. To one he fed polished rice, smuggled out of the kitchen; to the other he fed the unhusked *gaba*. The first group came down with beriberi to a bird. The second group remained healthy. Once rice husks had been added to its diet, the first group recovered.

The question was settled once and for all. Beriberi was not caused by something in the rice grain. On the contrary, it was caused because something was *not* in the rice grain.

Eijkman studied the existing literature on beriberi and learned that in 1880 a Japanese medical officer named Takaki, making experiments with the aid of the Japanese navy, had found that sailors on ships supplied with meat, vegetables and barley in addition to the inevitable rice, never developed beriberi. Takaki decided that beriberi was the result of insufficient protein. It was the wrong conclusion, but it kept beriberi out of the Japanese navy. Eijkman decided to make large-scale experiments of a similar nature, and got permission to use the disease-ridden prisons of the island as his testing ground. He ordered the use of *gaba* in exactly half the prisons. The inmates complained bitterly—but in exactly half the prisons beriberi was eradicated.

"There is present in rice polishings," Eijkman wrote, some years and some theories later, "a substance of a different nature from proteins, fats or salts, which is indispensable to health, and the lack of which causes nutritional polyneuritis." The effect of this lack he named "partial hunger."

Eijkman's theory was either ignored or ridiculed, in traditional fashion. His failure to extract the "anti-neuritic" factor, now called Vitamin B_1 or thiamine, did not help his cause. (It was a job on which highly trained chemists would work for years.) Although he is recognized today as one of the great men in the history of vitamin research, the significance of his early work was not fully credited until later investigators proved beyond doubt the existence of these substances "indispensable to health."

The experiments of Christiaan Eijkman and his immediate successors opened a hectic period in medical research. In the early days of the present century, the notion was fixed in most scientific minds that the only constituents of food necessary to life are proteins, carbohydrates, fats, and certain minerals. One could extract these substances, serve them in concentrated form, and thus save all the time and energy spent in cooking and eating. It was the work of a Cambridge professor of biochemistry named Frederick Gowland Hopkins to prove this uncivilized idea as false as it is unattractive.

Hopkins had nothing but scorn for the concentrated-food craze. In 1906 he set out to disprove it. He selected some fat, healthy white rats and separated them into two groups. To one group he fed a diet of "concentrated" food—pure protein, pure carbohydrate, pure fat, pure minerals—in the proportion and quantity which the concentrated-food champions considered vital. To the other group he fed exactly the same diet with a little fresh milk and yeast added. The second group maintained its good health and good spirits, but the cage next to it was soon a scene of desolation. The rats of the first group were losing weight, drooping visibly, and developing sore eyes and swollen feet. Hopkins published his classic report on these experiments in 1912, the same year in which a Polish-born chemist named Casimir Funk wrote that in his opinion beriberi, scurvy, rickets and pellagra were caused by dietary lack of "special substances which are of the nature of organic bases, which we will call *vitamines.*"

The "e" was soon dropped on etymological grounds. Funk later wrote: "I must admit that when I chose the name 'vitamine' I was well aware that these substances might later prove not to be of an amine nature. However, it was necessary for me to choose a name that would sound well and serve as a catchword."

He had chosen one that does both.

For about three years after Hopkins' report was published, a certain amount of confusion surrounded the new research. No one was sure just how many accessory food factors there were.

"There's only one!" some scientists argued. "It's found in butter-fat. But anyone who says it's found in yeast is crazy!"

"Of *course* there's only one!" other scientists retorted. "It's found in yeast. Anyone who says it's found in butterfat is out of his mind!"

"The growth-promoting factor is the same substance that prevents beriberi," said one group.

"No, no—the growth-promoting factor is the substance that prevents scurvy," said another.

"It prevents both!" said a third.

"Or neither?"

"Or maybe there are two factors——"

And for three years loud claims were made and then abandoned in favor of newer and more extravagant ones.

Two researchers named McCollum and Davis straightened things out. In 1915 they showed that dying rats on a purely synthetic diet could be rescued neither by butterfat alone nor by lactose alone. They needed both. "There are *two* factors necessary for growth," the two men decided. "One of them is soluble in fat, but not in water; the other is soluble in water, but not in fat."

The accessory food factors were now called "fat-soluble A" and "water-soluble B." Once their discoverers were convinced that they were really two distinct compounds, their names were changed to "Vitamin A" and "Vitamin B."

Vitamin A proved to be a powerful and necessary adjunct to life. Lack of it in the diet leads to a dreadful eye disease called xerophthalmia, and to night blindness; without it the body shows markedly lower resistance to every type of infection. It was found to be present in animal fats, in fish-liver oils, in many vegetables, in milk, cream, and a comfortable host of common foodstuffs.

In 1926, Vitamin B was broken down into compounds called B_1 and B_2, and about seven years later it was generally believed that B_2 was composed of more than one factor. At this writing there are six established and several other possible components in the B-complex. One of the most important of these is Vitamin B_{12}, which has revolutionized the treatment of pernicious anemia. It is the only known substance that will prevent and correct the dangerous neurological complications of the disease. In addition to the familiar Vitamins A, B, C and D, there are thirteen others which have been named. Chief among them is Vitamin K, which is essential in the liver's production of prothrombin, a vital element in the clotting of blood. Doses of the vitamin may be administered in cases of obstructive jaundice when bleeding tendencies are observed.

Dr. Joseph Goldberger, a brilliant Hungarian-born physician in the American Public Health Service, did research work on pellagra in 1926. He proved that the disease, which was prevalent in the South to the extent of 7000 deaths a year, was caused by a vitamin deficiency, as Casimir Funk had predicted. (The traditional diet in the pellagra belt is maize, molasses and salt pork.) Dr. Goldberger's work has solved one of the major regional-health problems of this country. The worst case of pellagra can now be cured in a matter of days by injections of Vitamin B_2.

Two investigators named Holst and Frölich found, in 1907, a new vitamin in lemon juice, as well as in potatoes, tomatoes, spinach, beans, and other vegetables and fruits. They called it Vitamin C. Not until 1932 was its chemical formula determined. It was then synthesized and named ascorbic acid. "Ascorbic" simply means scurvy-preventing. The shade of James Cook would have assented to that. Yes, something in lemon juice most certainly prevented scurvy.

The fourth disease which Casimir Funk, and Frederick Hopkins before him, had predicted was caused by the lack of a specific vitamin is rickets, a bone-distorting affliction of childhood. It is by no means uncommon even today, but it is as unnecessary a disease as beriberi or scurvy. From here on its prevention is the business of sociologists. Scientists have done their part of the job.

The name most closely associated with rickets research is that of Sir Edward Mellanby. In 1918 his dietary experiments on young dogs proved the relation between rickets and vitamin deficiency. For some time after his research was done, the anti-rachitic element which Zilva and Miura found in cod-liver oil was confused with Vitamin A. But further investigation showed that other foods known to be loaded with Vitamin A could not prevent rickets. The anti-rachitic vitamin was obviously a different one.

Germany was a pathetically fertile field for a study of the deficiency diseases. In 1919 the percentage of Berlin children with rickets was the highest in the memory of the city. The acute shortage of food made an imaginative investigator named Huldschinsky try the effect of treating rickets patients with an ultra-violet lamp. His experiments followed observations made twenty years before by Dr. T. A. Palm, who had written that rickets never attacked people who spent much of their lives in the sunlight. Huldschinsky found his ultra-violet lamp working wonders on the undernourished children of Berlin. It was later discovered that if one irradiated certain foods, including milk, and fed them to children with rickets, the effect was just as good. For a few months there was much buzzing about "bottled energy" and "mysterious emanations," but gradually the mystery of the anti-rachitic rays was solved. Both the human body and certain foodstuffs contain a substance which is quickly converted into the vitamin in the presence of sunlight.

The process of tracking down and closing in on the substance responsible for producing the vitamin was not unlike the methods used by policemen in investigating a group of suspects. It was a job that required seven years of the most meticulous patience: first, separating anti-rachitic foodstuffs into their chemical constituents; second, irradiating each group; third, testing the effect of each group on animals suffering from rickets.

Only the unlikely sterols, associates of fat, contained the hidden vitamin. Cholesterol, the most important member of the group, was immediately suspected. At first it reacted favorably to irradiation, but on further purification it suddenly stopped producing the vitamin altogether. Apparently the real vitamin-producer was something *in* the cholesterol, a powerful but minute impurity. A researcher came up with the key suggestion: irradiate all known sterols. One of them would probably prove to be the substance they were seeking.

One of them was; an obscure compound called ergosterol.

To irradiate ergosterol and extract from it the pure anti-rachitic substance was a weary job. Ergosterol turned out to be an unbelievably temperamental compound. Under ultra-violet treatment it persisted in breaking down into new compounds which formed other compounds by combining with each other, which in turn formed still other compounds. It was a chemist's nightmare from start to finish. Long before the last secret was understood, the vitamin itself became easily available in preparations of cod-liver oil, or simply in irradiated milk. When the pure substance, called Vitamin D, was finally extracted from ergosterol, it was found to exist in ridiculously small quantities. It has been estimated that in one tablespoon of cod-liver oil there is less than one millionth of an ounce of the pure vitamin. Consider the difference between a child with rickets and a healthy child, and it becomes abundantly clear that among those proverbial "little things that count," Vitamin D is one of them that counts the most.

Ever since the word "vitamin" was coined in 1912, the substances have become an important part of our civilization. First, they are big business. In 1944, at the peak of the vitamin boom, $200,000,000, representing one-third of the receipts on all drug sales, were paid across drug-store counters and through mail-order catalogues for different pills, capsules, tablets and liquids. The market has leveled off since then, but vitamins remain a multi-million-dollar industry.

Vitamins have also kept research laboratories buzzing in a variety of languages. We know a great deal more today than we did when the dispute raged over "fat-soluble A" and "water-soluble B," but fifty years hence our present knowledge of vitamin chemistry will probably be put in one paragraph of a textbook under the heading of "early work in the field."

Today there is a controversy over the full possibilities and the limitations of vitamin therapy. The truth must lie somewhere between two extremes. On the one hand, there are ecstatic claims made by advertising agencies to the effect that vitamins will not only prevent colds and banish "that tired feeling," but will also convert a wallflower into a prom queen. On the other, there is the conservative estimate of some doctors that vitamins have value in specific diseases, but are no help at all in sub-clinical conditions, most outstanding of which is "that tired feeling." Paradoxically, it is a tribute to the power of the mysterious chemicals that most people have no idea what their individual uses are, although the alphabet of vitamins is well known. The discovery of vitamins has brought about such a change in our standards of diet that the once commonplace deficiency diseases are now the most unnecessary of all afflictions.

part III

Of Men and Microbes

5

The Scientists Outlaw Diphtheria

"GENTLEMEN, come at once! Stop whatever you're doing and follow me!"

The two laboratory assistants looked up hurriedly from their microscopes. One did not often see the distinguished Professor Cohn rush into a room breathless, his coat-tails flying, his pince-nez teetering at the edge of his nose.

It occurred to the young men that a catastrophe of some sort had overtaken the Botanical Institute of Breslau, and they leaped to their feet, ready to be heroes. "Is the building on fire, Professor? Is the——"

"No, no." Cohn's face, already pink with exertion, was becoming maroon. "Go at once to Koch. The man has just shown us the greatest discovery ever made about bacteria!"

The assistants looked at one another doubtfully, then followed the professor out of the laboratory and down the hall. "Who'd he say?" one hissed into the ear of the other.

"Koch!"

"Koch?"

That country fellow from the province of Wollstein? The municipal health officer who had written to Professor Cohn a few weeks ago asking for an interview, and claiming that *he,* of all the unlikely people in Germany, could prove the process of development of bacteria? That Koch?

Save for mild amusement, the letter had made so little impression on the blasé young men that all thoughts of the country doctor and his claim had passed from their minds. Apparently, however, he had arrived.

Robert Koch had taken blood from a sheep dying of anthrax, injected it into a mouse, grown a new colony of anthrax bacilli from a snip of the mouse's tissue, injected the new bacilli into a new mouse, and then had recovered the bacilli from its dead body. It was really a very simple trick—which no one before him had ever managed to perform. For the first time the complete life cycle of the cause of a specific disease had been demonstrated, and all the doubts about the germ theory of disease transmission suddenly evaporated. Koch had given a unifying principle to bacteriology. The result of his labor was to provoke the most exhaustive program of medical research ever undertaken before or since his time. The great microbe hunt was on. It was to become an international *cause célèbre.*

The names of Pasteur and Koch are inextricably bound together by history, but in their lifetime the two men despised each other. Their respective students, following in the footsteps of the masters, carried on the feud. France and Germany waged a bloodless but impassioned war for priority in discovering the latest bacteria or the newest vaccine. Each triumphant announcement from one of them was greeted with disdain on the other side of the border; each hastily retracted claim was met with loud cries of "I told you so." But between them they tracked down an amazing list of mankillers in those two crowded decades which brought the last century to a close.

In 1884, just seven years after Koch's historic performance at Breslau, a hunt for a new microbe got under way. It began on a small scale because Friederich Löffler was a man of modest pretensions and little imagination. But it ended with a resounding victory over one of the most dangerous of man's natural enemies. To achieve this, an enormous number of people of different nationalities had to take a hand in the job: Frenchmen, Germans, Swiss, Austrians, Japanese, Englishmen and Americans, with the indirect help of people all over the world.

It started, however, in the basement of Robert Koch's laboratory in Schumann Street.

Friederich Löffler, in his systematic search for the microbe of diphtheria, had no difficulty in finding source material. Any morgue in any hospital in Berlin could provide him with it. No doctor fretted unduly if he lost half his diphtheria patients. A fifty-percent death rate was considered respectable, according to the grisly statistics of the day.

Löffler, as he went from bed to bed, gently scraping away bits of the leathery gray membrane which would eventually strangle half the children in the diphtheria ward, did not allow himself to be lured into useless speculation about cures or prevention of this catastrophe. He was concerned with only one question.

The year before, his colleague, Edwin Klebs, had found a new, unidentified microbe in the throat of a diphtheria victim. Was this club-shaped creature the specific cause of diphtheria or was it not?

Löffler had intended to be an army surgeon until a meeting with Robert Koch had changed the course of his life. Even as a civilian Löffler looked like a Prussian military man. His beard was trim, and his mustache bristled straight up at an angle of ninety degrees, which made him look older than his twenty-five years.

He thought like a military man, too: in straight lines. Young as he was, he had none of the imagination which sparked the after-hours talk around the Institut Pasteur. A Frenchman, peering at the blue bacillus, all of .000039 inches long, might have said, "Is it possible that this ridiculous creature is really the murderer that specializes in the strangling of children?" But Löffler simply investigated it.

Squinting into his microscope, Friederich Löffler said to his new glass-and-bottle-washer (now why, he wondered patiently, did he *always* get the greenest and most talkative of these would-be scientists): "You understand, of course, that this Klebs bacillus might have nothing whatsoever to do with diphtheria. Until we prove that it has, we shall assume that it has not."

"But Doctor——" The young man turned from the sink so abruptly that the sleeve of his lab coat made a clean sweep of the test-tubes which had been lying on the drainboard.

"My boy," Löffler said gently, "if you intend to make bacteriology your life's work, I suggest that you see about discarding the extra thumbs with which nature seems to have endowed you."

"Yes, Doctor." The assistant gulped, and deposited the last of the broken glass in the trash basket as quietly as it could be managed.

"You were saying?" Löffler reminded him.

"I was going to ask—even if the bacillus appears in most cases of diphtheria, how can you tell that it's the cause of the disease, and not just an effect?" The young man tossed off the query easily, as though the idea had just occured to him. If only he could impress his employer with his profound scientific curiosity—just once!

Löffler looked up from his microscope, obviously surprised. For two hideous seconds, the boy was convinced that his superior was going to heap reproaches on his head. Actually, he had succeeded beyond his greatest hope. Löffler was not only impressed, he was also temporarily distracted. That was more of an accomplishment than the boy realized.

"Herr Koch," Löffler said, absently stroking his luxuriant beard, "will ask the same question if I tell him that I believe the Klebs bacillus is the guilty party." Herr Koch, he thought, never failed to ask the very question calculated to collapse one's most beautifully blown-up theory. The mere fact of working under the same roof with him had its advantages. What man in his right mind would cut corners or jump to conclusions when he knew that he would eventually have to discuss his work with Robert Koch? Löffler then added hastily: "But don't take it into your head that your mind is even remotely like Robert Koch's!"

The boy raised a hand to protest the heresy, narrowly missing the water-distiller as he did so. "Oh, no," he said. "I just wondered—I mean, it just now came to me——"

"Yes, yes." Löffler removed the slide from the stage of his microscope and placed it gently in the slide box. It seemed curious to him that anyone, even this neophyte, should be ignorant of the law by which the Schumann Street laboratory lived and breathed. Löffler had so often heard his master outline his method of establishing the relation between a given disease and a suspected microbe that he could almost hear that forthright voice whispering in his ear.

He said to the boy, "Before we can definitely prove that any bacillus causes a given disease, we have to fulfill four conditions. First of all, we have to find the bacillus in every case of the disease we study—that's *every* case. Next, we have to grow the organism, taken from one such case, in a pure culture. Then, when we have a good, home-grown family, we must produce the disease in a healthy laboratory animal by infecting it from this culture. And fourth, we must find the suspected organism in the body of the diseased animal and grow it again in a pure culture. That completes the cycle." He added meditatively, "What a magnificent set of rules to follow!"

It is one of Friederich Löffler's principal claims to fame that he followed them to the letter, thus laying the groundwork for all future diphtheria research. "It is vain to speak of cures, or think of remedies," had said Galen, the great physician of Rome, "until such time as we have considered the causes." It was an argument as valid in 1884 as it had been in 200 A.D.

Löffler's work was to establish the cause of diphtheria. He used an alkaline methylene blue stain, still called by his name, to show up the club-shaped bacillus on his slides. After numerous trials and errors, he succeeded in growing the temperamental creature on a solidified blood-serum base. Then, with the new culture, he killed off a convincing number of guinea-pigs—twenty-three—and from the corpses he recovered and grew the blue-staining descendants of the original bacilli.

To a less cautious man, the case would have been proved overwhelmingly. But Löffler was not satisfied by the findings of his classic research. His paper describing the work was couched in such modest language that no one quite realized how far-reaching the discovery would be. Not for two years did Löffler resolve his doubts and announce unconditionally: "The Klebs bacillus is the sole and specific cause of diphtheria." It became the Klebs-Löffler bacillus. It is still known by that name.

Throughout his researches, one question had puzzled Löffler beyond all others. He had long ago lost count of the number of corpses, human and animal, which he had almost ripped to shreds in his search for the microbe. Yet in none of them had he ever found the bacillus circulating in the body, not even in cases of death resulting from paralysis of the heart. The pattern was so regular as to be monotonous. In his post-mortem examinations of human victims, the creatures were found only around the inflamed membrane of the throat; in laboratory animals, they were found only at the spot where he had injected them.

"It's ridiculous," he said to his assistant. "These creatures positively cannot travel. They are literally glued to the spot where they're produced. But they *can* cause paralysis of the heart muscles. In fact, they can kill about as effectively as any microbe in existence."

"Do any other bacteria work that way?"

"None that we know about yet."

"But it doesn't seem possible. If the thing can move——"

"My dear boy, Löffler protested, "when you say that something clearly observable in nature is impossible, at least try to sound as though you didn't mean it!"

"But do *you* know how it works?"

Löffler thought he knew how it worked, but he was a cautious man. Later he stated this theory in print, very definitely before anyone else had ever stated it. The proof of this theory, however, he left to others—as it turned out, to a couple of Frenchmen.

He said to the boy, "It stands to reason, since the creature cannot move itself, but can produce paralysis of the heart——"

"—that it must produce a poison in its body and pour it out into the blood stream of the host," Emile Roux said excitedly. He tended to talk even faster than usual when on his favorite subject. Roux was thirty-five years old, thin-faced and sad-eyed. But native enthusiasm was surging in his blood. It would keep him going for more years of heroic exhaustion than he had been built for.

Since his twenty-fifth year, the young man had been the most valuable of all Pasteur's disciples, and now that the old man himself was failing it was Roux who guided the affairs of the Institut Pasteur from behind the scenes.

Out of the medical problems which were studies at the Institute, diphtheria had become the obsession of Emile Roux. Any doctor with a heart was bound to be disturbed by the ferocity of diphtheria in 1888, when the disease was raging through the city in an epidemic more violent than the oldest men of the Institute could remember. Everyone regretted the existence of diphtheria. But it drove Emile Roux to a fine frenzy.

"Produce a poison and pour it into the blood stream," repeated Yersin, the brilliant young Swiss scientist who had joined forces with Roux in the new diphtheria experiments. "We've said it so many times that one might almost think we were trying to convince ourselves."

Roux, in a particularly pessimistic mood, shrugged his drooping shoulders. "It is hard," he said, "to go about looking for something that quite possibly does not exist. And no one has ever found such a poison circulating." Löffler, in identifying the bacillus, had been guided by Koch's methods as definitely as though the master had been standing behind him, calling out his next move. But Roux and Yersin had only the depressing knowledge that they were completely on their own.

So far, the two researchers had only one result to show for their efforts: a trash basket full of dead guinea pigs, used in repeating Löffler's experiments. The dead animals contributed little to their knowledge. They had been shot full of diphtheria microbes. They had been expected to die, and they had died. The deadly microbes had been recovered from their bodies only at the exact site of entrance. The same old story.

"Now," said Roux, "there is one thing we need to settle the question, and that is the body of a guinea pig—just one guinea pig—that has died of diphtheria without ever coming near a diphtheria microbe."

"One dead guinea pig," Yersin repeated, stretching his back wearily. He glanced at the grisly trash basket which the janitor was just removing. "A rather curious wish to be the most important one in life." He was smiling, but by the end of the next two weeks he would make the same comment without smiling at all.

Roux prepared a pure, flourishing culture of diphtheria bacilli and incubated it for a week. During that time, he and Yersin believed, the bacilli would manufacture and exude the poisonous substance which circulated through the body of a person stricken with the disease.

In a corner of the laboratory, Roux and Yersin had put together a startling piece of equipment: a filter made of porcelain so fine that any solid object—even one as small as a diphtheria bacillus—could not pass through its grain. Neither, as it developed, could the liquid. For hours of agonizing doubt the two men, suddenly aware of their deficiencies as mechanics, fussed over the gadget while the broth, the deadliest brew ever concocted, splashed stubbornly around the top of the filter. Finally they forced the liquid through by rigging up an air-pressure pump.

They were ready to go now, and almost frantic with eagerness to get to the real business of the experiment. But they forced themselves to slow down and examine sample after sample of the filtrate to see whether any bacilli had somehow sneaked through.

Roux tossed the last slide into the sink and said, "No—this is as clear as a filtrate can be. Not a trace of the bacilli. Whatever harm the broth does is its own responsibility."

"Shall we give it a try?" his colleague said. "I have the syringe sterilized."

"Sterilize it again."

"Wh——?"

"I have suddenly become a fanatic," Roux said.

Yersin shrugged. "We're all fanatics," he replied. "If we weren't, we wouldn't last in this place a week." He resterilized the syringe.

Roux injected a few cubic centimeters of the broth

into a guinea pig. "This is a small dose," he said, "but if the broth is really full of poison, it's enough to kill one little animal. In two days, now——"

The little animal, as it developed, had other ideas on the subject. It remained in extraordinarily good spirits, its health exactly as it had been forty-eight hours before. Seventy-two hours later, Roux was forced to concede that the shot had had no effect whatever.

Grimly he refilled his syringe, this time doubling the amount of filtrate. "If *this* much doesn't do it," he said, "then we might as well forget all this business about microbes that pour poison into the blood stream."

Two days later, tripling the dose and injecting it into the animal, he had nothing at all to say.

Four days after that, having tripled the tripled dose without results, he said flatly, "It's no good. There's nothing in the filtrate that's going to give anybody diphtheria."

There *must* be, he said to himself. The microbe *does* produce a poison. I know it does. It must be in the broth.

"But it so obviously isn't," he snapped, answering himself aloud, to the perplexity of Yersin.

"We can try it once more, anyway," the latter said doubtfully, eyeing the contented animal with distaste.

Roux considered the situation for an indecisive moment, then walked over to the door and locked it. What he was about to do was mad. Not even inspired madness should have any witnesses. "*Bien,*" he said. "Once more."

He sterilized a large syringe and measured 35cc. of the filtrate. Thirty-five cubic centimeters! Over one fluid ounce. Visualize the amount of liquid held by three large tablespoons; then recall the size of the average guinea pig. "He can't complain this time," Roux said bitterly. "Even if he doesn't die of diphtheria, he'll probably burst in the process of trying. Oh, this is a wonderfully precise experiment! Robert Koch would give half his beard to get wind of how we do things around here."

Yersin sighed. "Now what?" he inquired.

"Now I'm going home. I can't bear to watch this animal running around, bursting with health, and making fools out of us."

But the guinea pig had had its last opportunity for doing so. The next morning it was obviously diphtheretic, and five days later it was dead.

"Thirty-five cc. to kill one guinea pig!" Yersin said, looking up from his careful scrutiny of the corpse. "Either the guinea pig was a veritable Hercules among guinea pigs, or our broth was not very well cooked."

"By all means," Roux said emphatically, "let us see about changing the recipe."

Now that they knew what they were doing they overcame their technical problems with ease. Soon, after changing the composition of the incubating broth and lengthening the cooking time, they obtained a poison so concentrated that .8cc. would kill a guinea pig in two days.

The unorthodox laboratory techniques of Roux and Yersin had brought diphtheria research to a critical point. The causes had now ceased to be theoretical; they were hard, indisputable facts. It was time to speak of cures and think of remedies, according to Galen.

Emil von Behring worked a few doors down from the room in which Friederich Löffler, still cautious, still doubtful, was doggedly staining slides. Behring himself was busy shooting a dying guinea pig full of iodine trichloride. For weeks he had been hard at work slaughtering guinea pigs, filling them first with diphtheria toxin, then with whatever chemical was currently engaging his attention.

This chemical warfare appealed to Behring and to most of the German scientists. "It is logical," they said. "Whatever is logical is good science. If chemicals will kill germs in the test-tube, why should they not kill germs in the body?"

The only trouble was the better-than-average chance that the chemicals would kill the patient while getting rid of the germs. Thus far, Emil Behring's chemicals had succeeded in doing only that to the guinea pigs. There was little choice between the disease and the remedy.

Iodine trichloride was different. It narrowly missed

killing the guinea pig, but it most decidedly killed whatever diphtheria germs (now called *Corynebacteria*) were in him.

Behring was too realistic to believe even for a moment that he had found a practical cure for diphtheria. "Can one save a child from death by scalding his veins with a poison which is as dangerous in its way as the toxin of diphtheria?" he asked himself. The iodine-trichloride experiment would have been unimportant save for one thing: Emil Behring now had a laboratory animal which had recovered from diphtheria.

Everyone knew that people who had once had diphtheria were safe from it for the rest of their lives. That fact had been obvious through years of observation. But what was behind this concession of nature, Behring wondered.

"Do you suppose that this poor creature is now immune to diphtheria?" he asked, thinking out loud, but addressing his thoughts to his colleague Fränkel.

"Why not? Wouldn't you be?"

"I don't know. I've never had diphtheria that was artificially induced and artificially cured. And I don't suppose it would prove very much if this animal *is* immune. But——" Behring filled a syringe with a fresh culture of *Corynebacteria,* and pumped the uncomplaining guinea pig full of it.

Nothing happened.

He tried injecting the animal with pure toxin. Still nothing happened. He repeated the experiment he had originated on other animals. Those which were not killed, either by the disease or by the iodine trichloride, were safe from a second attack of diphtheria.

"What protects them the second time that wasn't around to protect them the first time?" Behring asked himself. The science of immunology dates from that moment of curiosity.

"Whatever it is," he reasoned, "is certainly located in the blood stream, where the toxin itself circulates. Would it work *outside* the body that originally produced it?"

From his convalescent guinea pigs he drew some blood, and separated the clear serum from the cells. To the serum he added an equal amount of deadly pure toxin, calculated to kill any nonimmune guinea pig in forty-eight hours. He injected the mixture into the veins of a fresh laboratory animal. The guinea pig was bothered by it no more than by the prick of a needle.

Behring, suddenly in possession of an animal that had no right to be alive, according to the science of the day, pondered his next move with care. Although he was a man given to wilder flights of fancy than most of his colleagues, he kept his head. In Koch's laboratory no discovery was credited even with grudging attention until it had been subjected to a systematic debunking by the entire staff. It took Behring only a few moments' thought to evolve the next step.

"Draw 5cc. of blood from a guinea pig," he told his assistant, "and separate the serum from the cells."

"From one of these?" the assistant asked him, nodding at the cage where the immune animals were kept.

"No, no. From a new one!" Behring laughed. "From one that hasn't even been inside the laboratory."

To the blood serum of this animal Behring added some diphtheria toxin. He injected the mixture into several nonimmune guinea pigs. Two days later, as he stood with his colleagues observing the dead bodies of these animals, he said to Robert Koch, "Blood serum from an immune animal neutralizes the toxin of diphtheria, but blood serum from a nonimmune animal does not."

"Now," said Koch, "you must prove it forward as well as backward. See what happens when you provide the prevention first and then the poison."

Behring did. He gave serum first, then toxin, to a fresh guinea pig. He found that he could not determine which shot affected the animal less. The unimpressionable laboratory rejoiced as it had never rejoiced before.

Few scientific communications have been of so much significance to so many people as the paper published in the *German Medical Journal* on December 4, 1890: "On the Production of Diphtheria Immunity and Tetanus Immunity in Animals." The paper, written by Behring in collaboration with the Japanese bacteriologist, Kitasato, a great name in tetanus research, stated for the first time the underlying principle of immunity. "The immunity of animals," they wrote, ". . . consists in the power of the cell-free blood to render innocuous the toxic substances which the . . . bacillus produces." How was it that some people were immune to diphtheria and some were not? In the blood of the lucky immunes there circulated a mysterious substance, hitherto unsuspected, which could neutralize the toxins as fast as they were produced. In a footnote, the two men suggested the name "antitoxin."

What about the unlucky ones, Behring asked himself, who have so little antitoxin in their blood that they have *no* protection against the disease? What about a patient already dying of diphtheria? Would antitoxin given after, not before the toxin, cure diphtheria as well as prevent it?

He abandoned the line of research which would have led him to discover the method of widespread prevention. The cure! That was the spectacular idea which now obsessed him. If a German scientist could come through with a cure for the most vicious disease on earth . . .

Behring sent the supply office a requisition for the largest supply of guinea pigs he had ever ordered at one time. To all of them he gave a lethal shot of toxin. And then, when they were lying on their backs, quietly dying of diphtheria, he gave exactly half of them a shot of antitoxin. The other half, the control group, he left alone.

All the animals in the control goup died; most, but not all of the animals in the other group recovered. Although the favorable results were far from the hundred percent mark, Behring decided that the time had come to move his experiments out of the laboratory and into the hospital.

The first trial of the antitoxin on human beings is supposed to have been made on Christmas Eve. Sadly enough, that experiment failed, despite its dramatic timing. But others succeeded. In the Von Bergmann clinic in Berlin, strange things began happening to the diphtheria mortality rate. Unconvincing as those early experiments were, by our standards, they aroused great excitement. Behring was sure that the failure of antitoxin, provided it was given early enough in the disease, meant simply that the antitoxin was not strong enough. While he and his associates kept at this line of research, the center of activity again shifted. It returned to Paris and there progressed under the direction of Emile Roux, the Frenchman who had read Behring's earth-shaking reports with greater happiness than anyone else in the world.

"Horses!" said Roux. "Get me some horses, and let us stop this foolishness with guinea pigs!"

He wanted serum by the bucket, not by the drop.

And he wanted the most effective, the most dependable serum in Europe. Nothing less could satisfy him.

Behring had showed the world how it could be done. Mix diphtheria bacilli with iodine trichloride, or any chemical which would take most of the fight out of them; then inject small, gradually increasing doses of the creatures into an animal. The bacteria would be too weak to do much damage, but the body, stimulated by their presence, would begin producing antitoxin. And eventually not even otherwise lethal doses of pure toxin would bother it.

Emile Roux was, as usual, in a fever of excitement. The classic calm with which Behring had proceeded in his investigations was not for the volatile Frenchman. To him every day spent in puttering about the laboratory meant another day of needless deaths in the hospital. Emil von Behring said that the antitoxin which he produced in the bodies of laboratory animals might save children who were dying of diphtheria. That was good enough for Emile Roux. If he could have his way, every diphtheria-stricken child in Paris would have serum as quickly as he could get his hands on the precious stuff.

"Horses!" he demanded. They were animals with capacious blood vessels, with plenty of blood to spare . . . his imagination was fired. In his haste to make every minute count double, he worked out immunization methods calculated to produce the strongest serum yet known. And then on February 1, 1894, he strode into the Paris Children's Hospital. His assistants came behind him carrying gallon jars full of the straw-colored horse serum.

Four hundred forty-eight children were in the diphtheria ward. According to the time-tested method of control groups, 224 of them should have been given the antitoxin. Then, by comparing the relative mortality rates in the two groups, the question of the serum's value would have been answered definitively.

Hours later, Roux left the hospital with empty jars and with no records at all. There were none to be kept. Of the 448 children, 448 had been given injections of serum. He had nothing to do now but wait.

In September he reported his experiment to a medical congress in Budapest. Of the cases treated, he told his colleagues, 339 had recovered.

Skeptics in the audience muttered, "How does he know they wouldn't have recovered even without his horse serum?"

His figures, Roux went on, would have been more convincing if he had treated only half the diphtheria patients in the Children's Hospital. But he had not found it in his heart to sacrifice lives in order to create statistics. He was a doctor, not a mathematician. In any case, he hedged, he did have a sort of control. At the Hôpital Trousseau, where use of the serum had not been permitted, 316 diphtheria patients had died out of the 520 who had been admitted. This 60 per cent mortality, as contrasted with the 24.5 per cent death rate at the Children's Hospital, seemed to him to make a case for antitoxin.

The Budapest Congress agreed heartily. To a man, the assembled doctors rose to their feet and cheered for Emile Roux, Emil von Behring, and Friederich Löffler; for Klebs, Koch, Kitasato, Yersin, Pasteur, and all their associates and assistants down to the last dead guinea pig.

One of the spectators was so shaken by Roux's report that he rushed to the nearest telegraph office and sent an urgent cable to New York City. He was Dr. Herman Biggs, the Health Commissioner of that port.

"Cable for you, Doc. From—lemme see—from *Budapest*! Who do you know in Budapest?" the awed Western Union messenger asked.

"My boss is there," answered Dr. Park.

In his Bleecker Street laboratory William Hallock Park, Assistant Health Commissioner, opened the cable and read:

DIPHTHERIA ANTITOXIN SUCCESS. BEGIN TO PRODUCE.

BIGGS

Dr. Park was a young man of decisive mind. He put the cable into a desk drawer and walked over to the nearest livery stable. He said, "I want to buy a horse."

This direct approach was the first step in the diphtheria-control program of New York City. By the turn of the century, the whole world would be imitating its methods.

What figures the public-health statisticians could

reel off as the work slowly picked up momentum! The year before the introduction of antitoxin, 134 out of every 100,000 residents of New York City had died of diphtheria. In 1900, early in the history of antitoxin, the figure had dropped to 54 deaths per 100,000. During the war years, as prejudice against the new treatment gradually diminished, only 29 diphtheria deaths per 100,000 occurred.

The pattern of the New York figures was repeated in other cities, but few public-health officers had early results as startling as Park's. They stemmed from the lucky production of an extraordinarily vital serum—one of the happy accidents which occasionally come along to help "the mind that is prepared," in Pasteur's phrase. In this case the mind involved was entirely prepared. It belonged to a distinguished American bacteriologist, Dr. Anna Williams, who was to become Park's chief collaborator. One day, shortly after her appointment to the Health Department laboratory as an assistant, Dr. Williams was making a routine examination of cultures grown from cases of suspected diphtheria. One of these cultures, taken from a mild, tonsillar diphtheria, she deposited in her Number Eight test-tube. The most cursory examination showed the alert doctor that here was no ordinary family of microbes. It was almost unbelievably active—a constant producer of the strongest toxin she had ever encountered.

This strain, which came to be called simply Park-Williams Number Eight, was soon the official toxin-producer of the laboratory. The virulent culture was dripped into the veins of the immune laboratory horses, and all over their bodies cells responded to the fearful challenge of the Number Eight bacilli. And the antitoxin produced to combat it was itself far more powerful than other antitoxins. Today descendants of the original family of Park-Williams Number Eight bacilli are still hard at work yielding toxin in laboratories all over the world.

Marvelous as his figures were, Park was not satisfied by them. Behring and Roux had considered the curative powers of the antitoxin to be its most important property. But Park was a public-health doctor, and this made him a more realistic thinker than either of his European colleagues. As a doctor, Park was pleased by the high percentage of cures effected by the antitoxin. As a public-health official, he was dissatisfied by the necessity for cure. Prevention was his goal, and only total prevention would satisfy him.

It had been known from the earliest of Behring's experiments that the immunity conferred by antitoxin was not permanent. There was no mystery in this. If blood from one species of animal is injected into a second species, the foreign blood will be eliminated as quickly as possible by the protesting body. Therefore horse-serum did not long survive in human arteries.

"Now," Park said to himself, "I have to make the human body produce its own antitoxin in its own blood serum. That way it should always be immune."

A fine idea, in principle. How did one put it into practice? Antitoxin was produced in horses that were already immune by injecting them with gradually increasing amounts of diphtheria toxin. Dr. Park closed his eyes and imagined himself telling a P.T.A. meeting that he intended to start shooting nonimmune children full of diphtheria toxin in gradually increasing doses over a period of six weeks. He shuddered.

There was another possibility. Quite properly, the idea had first been suggested by one of Koch's men. Paul Ehrlich, the charmingly eccentric researcher who later produced the first known cure for syphilis, had done a lot of thinking on the subject of immunity. "If one gives a *mixture* of toxin and antitoxin," Ehrlich had concluded, "one will produce an active, lasting immunity against diphtheria by 'educating' the body to respond to any future attacks by the toxin." In Boston Theobald Smith, the first great American bacteriologist, was saying the same thing. Park had at hand a valuable ally for the testing of the Ehrlich-Smith theory: the energetic Bacilli Number Eight. To lessen the virulence of that toxin he usually mixed it with antitoxin before injecting it into his horses. He had found that no matter how completely neutralized the Number Eight was before injection, it still produced a high degree of immunity in animals. Would it do the same for animals that had no immunity? It would. It would also, Dr. Park and his associates discovered, do the same for nonimmune human beings. Toward the end of the war years came the startling announcement that three shots of a toxin-antitoxin mixture would produce harmless, permanent immunity to diphtheria in human beings.

A few years later a variation was introduced. As it was discovered, the toxin is an unstable substance. Once filtered from the producing microbe it changes its composition quickly and becomes a harmless liquid with only one of its former properties. Injected into the body, it calls out all the antitoxin reserve of the body cells. "Toxoid," as the filtered culture was named, remains the most effective means known of producing immunity. It seemed that nature was doing her apologetic best to make up to the human race for having created the *Corynebacterium diphtheriae* in the first place.

One more step and the circuit would be closed. Dr. Park was determined to inoculate every nonimmune person in New York. He knew that half the children and four-fifths of the adult population were already immune. Theoretically one could inoculate everybody in sight to catch all those who were not immune. Actually it was an impractical idea. In addition to the mere physical labor involved, there was the matter of human nature to contend with. At that time, an aura of fear and prejudice surrounded the idea of antitoxin. There was a touch of black magic about the business, a great many people felt. Park knew that the schools were the greatest ally of the Health Department in overcoming public distrust of diphtheria immunization. He longed for a simple, painless way to test immunity.

In 1908 the answer came from an Austrian, Dr. Bela Schick, who had moved his home to the United States and taken up his career as a pediatrician with the Health Department. Dr. Schick devised the familiar test, which now bears his name, of scratching a minute amount of toxin under the skin and observing the surface reaction. If the person tested is already immune, there will be sufficient antitoxin present in his body to neutralize the toxin immediately. But if he is nonimmune and has no antitoxin on hand, then the scratch will cause slight local irritation, a distress signal no more violent than a red lump.

The utmost tact, diplomacy and perseverance were required before the Board of Health and the Board of Education extracted anything approaching universal consent from parents to the immunization of their children. New York statistics on deaths caused by diphtheria show a marked decline when immunization became widespread: from 1920 to 1924, just after the adoption of toxin-antitoxin and toxoid inoculation, the death rate dropped to 14 per 100,000; from 1930 to 1934, after the method had gained public acceptance, there were 2.2 deaths per 100,000. In 1935, the rate hit 0.9.

England suffered an acute rise in its diphtheria death rate during the last war. Its experience led to new researches, largely by English scientists, on the classification of diphtheria microbes as *gravis* and *mitis* —serious and mild—and on appropriate changes in the makeup of the serum. Some work remains to be done in this field. As long as one person a year dies of diphtheria, there is room for improvement.

6

War on Yellow Fever

THE captain of the transport waved a beefy hand and said, "There she is, Major! Greatest sight in the world, and I've seen them all!"

The sight was Havana harbor. The Major, who was seasick, also thought the sight the greatest in the world. Any dry land would have seemed great. He clutched the railing of the ship and averted his eyes from the dizzily rolling coastline.

"Fine-looking harbor," he said thickly.

"Wonderful little place. Been down before?"

"Once."

"Wouldn't live any place but Cuba—that is, if I ever lived in *any* place longer'n a week," the Captain announced, laughing uproariously for reasons which escaped the pallid Major. "I'd give you New York, Philadelphia, Boston, and Chicago any day of the year in exchange for Havana!" he went on.

The Major felt inclined to point out that he was not in a position to drive the bargain, but he said instead, "Too many bugs."

The Captain raised his eyes eloquently, as though he were calling for heavenly patience, and said, "Few little mosquitoes never hurt a grown man yet, did they? Why, Major, do you know that down here you can get a whole bunch of bananas for one American nickel, and——"

The Major, blinking into the sun-streaked coastline, interrupted him. "Isn't that a fire in the harbor?" he asked.

"Probably another yellow-jack cargo." The naval officer glanced casually in the direction indicated. "We have enough trouble with yellow jack right now without importing it! Most likely a ship in from Barbados."

Although in 1900 the sight of a ship's cargo being burned on suspicion of yellow fever was not so common as it had been twenty years before, it was by no means a novelty, particularly in times of epidemic, and an epidemic was currently raging in Cuba.

"How were things when you left?" the Major inquired.

The Captain shrugged indifferently. "Fresh outbreak in the barracks, they say. Nothing too special this time. Same old story. Part of living, Major. Part of living!"

Major Walter Reed doubted strongly that yellow fever was an essential part of life in the twentieth century, even though the century was only seven months old, but he did not feel up to arguing the point.

The Captain said, "I hear some sort of congressional committee's been appointed to find out how to cure yellow jack." He seemed pleased by the idea. "That's what I love about Congress," he went on, chuckling. "All they have to do is form a committee and they think they can stop the sun from coming up. If I were Teddy Roosevelt——"

"You don't think it's worth a try?" the Major inquired.

"What? Forming a committee to cure yellow jack? No way to stop yellow jack, Major. You may be in the medical corps, but *I'm* telling you. I've seen too much of it to know. Just keep burning up bedding, and keep your fingers crossed, and after that——"

A hail from the quarter-deck interrupted him. He shouted back an unintelligible order and then said, "See you ashore, Major. Hope you enjoy your stay, and don't let our mosquitoes worry you! They're part of the scenery. Tourists like 'em!" He stamped off, bellowing additional advice to the quarter-deck. Reed sighed with relief, then winced as the cross currents of the channel bounced the ship.

Fighting Indians in Arizona had been nothing like this, the Major thought, wondering whether his face could possibly look as sick as he felt. He wondered too whether he could accomplish anything in Cuba which would be worth the effort of getting down there. In the self-pitying mood which always accompanies sea sickness, he doubted it. The Captain was probably right—in everything except his statement of the actual fact. No committee of Congress had been formed to cure yellow fever. Congress was involved only in the matter of appropriations. What had been formed was an army commission to investigate the unknown causes of yellow fever. Major Walter Reed was at its head.

As he collected his belongings in his cabin, Major Reed found himself remembering snatches of the burly Captain's conversation. The man's closing words had stayed with him. "Just keep burning . . . and keep your fingers crossed." The Captain's formula was not as much over-simplified as it sounded. In actual fact, there was nothing else one could do about yellow fever.

Yellow fever, the plague bequeathed to America by the African slave trade, struck in the United States eighty-six times between 1668, the year in which it made its first recorded appearance, and 1900. It was by nature a tropical disease, but it was not much concerned with climatic conditions. Few cities from Boston to Havana had escaped it completely. In Memphis, the epidemic of 1878 killed 5000 people in two weeks, and drove 30,000 more out of the stricken city. That epidemic was seventy-two years ago. Five and a half million people who are still alive today were alive then. From a historian's point of view it was a recent event.

How is it that today our chances for contracting the disease are so slight that the one case recently reported in this country made headlines as a medical curiosity? What has become of yellow fever in so short a time?

"Well, gentlemen, where do we start?"

The United States Army Yellow Fever Commission, newly convened on the porch of the officers' mess, was composed of four men: Walter Reed himself; James Carroll, a one-time Canadian backwoodsman who had joined the army as a private, and had taken up medicine twelve years later; Aristide Agramonte, a Cuban-born pathologist from Columbia University; and Jesse Lazear, an American physician. They got on very well with each other, an unusual circumstance in medical history. There were no antipathies, no petty jealousies; when their research was done, there was no tearing of hair and gnashing of teeth over who had thought of what first.

"Oh, we could begin anywhere," Carroll answered pessimistically, "because we'll be going in circles anyway."

"The beauty of yellow-fever research," the young Lazear announced, stroking his luxuriant beard in a scholarly manner, "is that you don't get all confused figuring up what you know about it. You just have to keep track of what you *don't* know about it."

"That's easy," Carroll said. "Things we don't know about yellow fever: what causes it? how is it spread? how can it be prevented from spreading? how do you cure it?"

Reed laughed. "You make it all sound so simple. There's a large sea-going man on the island who has it all figured out, though. Burn up all the bedding and keep your fingers crossed!"

It suddenly occurred to him that it had taken a hundred years to evolve even this piece of homespun advice.

Yellow fever had been very much in evidence for some four hundred years, but not until the end of the eighteenth century had it begun to arouse any degree of scientific interest. Up to that time, most people had looked upon it as just another of life's misfortunes. But in 1793 the city of Philadelphia, the most modern city in the country, was almost wiped out by an epidemic of terrifying proportions. It became a matter of professional necessity for every doctor to range himself on one side of the yellow-fever controversy or the other. The question could not have been more straightforward: Is yellow fever contagious, or is it not?

The men who believed it was contagious held that the disease was spread from person to person by direct contact. The "non-contagious" school avowed fiercely that it generated itself "spontaneously," under proper conditions of heat and filth, and that it could not be spread by direct contact. For eighty-five years the dispute raged, but eventually a compromise view was reached.

About the time of the 1878 epidemic doctors began to believe that yellow fever occupied a peculiar place between contagious and non-contagious diseases. It was not spread by direct contact like smallpox, they said, for the "emanations" from the sick required a warm, dark place in which to grow strong enough to infect the next comer. The sick man himself was harmless. But his bedding, his clothing, his furniture, any of his material possessions, in fact—these were the villains. The term *fomites*—a Latin word meaning substances capable of transmitting contagion—came into use.

Let a ship out of a town even remotely suspected of infection drop anchor in any harbor, and its cargo was immediately dumped on the wharf and burned. The cargo was no longer cargo. It had become *fomites.* The wholesale destruction of houses and the personal property of yellow-fever victims was almost inevitable. According to the statisticians of the time, the 1878 epidemic cost the country not less than $100,000,000. New Orleans alone claimed a loss of $10,000,000. Consider the value of the dollar in 1878!

The *fomites* theory entrenched itself. It seemed the only way to explain the almost whimsical methods by which the disease spread. It could hardly be said to spread at all. It jumped. "It often leaves a block or house intact," wrote one observer in 1878, "going around it and attacking those beyond with no assignable reason. A thin board partition seems to have stopped it on Governor's Island, in 1856, and an instance is related where it attacked the sailors in all the berths of one side of a ship before crossing to the other. Such apparent vagaries, in the present state of our knowledge, are inexplicable."

Curious that a personnel shake-up in Washington should be the first step in solving the "inexplicable" problem.

In 1893 the Surgeon-General of the army died. He had been an elderly, conservative gentleman, with no patience in him when it came to newfangled, European notions about germs. Germs were all right in their place, the general thought, but they had nothing to do with the United States Army. Good paper work kept an army office going, not fancy theories.

When the old general died, he was succeeded by a man who could not have been a greater study in contrast if he had come from the moon. George Miller Sternberg, our first real hero in the battle against yellow fever, was a doctor first and an army officer second. He was, specifically, a bacteriologist, as devoted to the germ theory of disease as the old man had been opposed to it. As Surgeon-General he was in a position to convert his zeal for research into action backed both by authority and appropriation. And the problem nearest to his heart was yellow fever, a disease over which he had been fuming for twenty years.

In July of 1897, the *British Medical Journal* printed the announcement that an Italian researcher, Giuseppe Sanarelli, had discovered the specific cause of yellow fever, a bacillus which he called *icteroides*. This news filled Dr. Sternberg full of hope. He appointed Walter Reed, who was then working at Johns Hopkins, to investigate the Sanarelli claims. Reed's associate in the work was John Carroll, an army surgeon whom he had met in the university laboratories.

After months of intensive work, they reported negative results. *Bacillus icteroides*, the army men announced, was a variety of the hog-cholera bacillus. So far as they could tell it had no connection at all with yellow fever. Sanarelli retorted that the U.S. Army was obviously out to get him, and made baleful innuendoes about the research technique of Reed and Carroll.

The feud over *B. icteroides* was raging when a sudden, fierce epidemic of yellow fever broke out among the American troops stationed in Havana. General Sternberg decided that the time for half measures had passed. He appointed a commission to proceed at once to Cuba and get to work on yellow fever.

Reed sighed inaudibly and said, "Still, we have to start somewhere, and with something we can say yes or no to."

"Like *Bacillus icteroides*? I'll say no to that right now," Lazear announced, frowning. "Good-for-nothing hog-cholera germ trying to get famous!"

"General Sternberg thinks one more go at it might not be a bad idea," Reed said. "Tomorrow we start making cultures. Believe me, the sooner we convince everybody that the Sanarelli bug is a fraud, the happier I'll be, and the sooner we can get down to serious work."

"There's only one person you'll never convince," said Carroll. "Sanarelli."

Reed smiled and revolved the glass in his hand slowly. The gentle clink-clink of ice was a comfortable sound in the steaming July night. "I have a feeling," he said, "that this is the last night we'll spend sitting around. It's pleasant while it lasts. If——"

A grimly efficient aide burst into the porch. "Sorry to disturb you, Major, but I'd like to get these reports out for the morning mail ship. Do you mind?"

"Reports?"

"Requisitions for laboratory supplies. Oh, the supplies are here all right, but we have to sign the receipts in quadruplicate, you know. One for our files, one for the Governor-General, one for the Surgeon-General's office, one for——"

"Never mind! I'll sign." Reed seized the proffered pen. When the aide had scurried out, he chuckled. "Why did I ever join the army?" he inquired, lowering his voice confidentially.

"Why did you, Major?" Lazear asked him. "It's not the usual place to look for a crack bacteriologist."

Reed blinked. "Come to think of it," he said, "I joined the army so I could get married."

Agramonte laughed. "Isn't it more usual to join the army to get out of getting married?"

"Well, I was an exceptional case, then." He flicked a passing mosquito from his wrist and inspected the screening of the porch with a critical eye. Suddenly he realized that his junior officers were looking at him expectantly. He sighed good-naturedly and said, "Briefly, I was so young when I got out of medical school that no one in his right mind would let me take out a splinter. So I traipsed up North from Virginia and did some extra work at Bellevue Hospital in New York. I still couldn't seem to interest any patients in my services, but I found just the job I was looking for! It was training I recommend highly for any young doctor." He chuckled quietly.

"Like what?" Agramonte said.

"Municipal Health Inspector of the Borough of Brooklyn! There's not much you can't learn in Brooklyn," he added parenthetically.

"How long did it last?" Lazear asked, somewhat awed.

"Not long. One day—it was in 1874, as I remember—I made a spur-of-the-moment visit to a little place in North Carolina." Reed shook his head, smiling. "I have the feeling that if I hadn't been in North Carolina that week end I wouldn't be in Cuba today."

"That can only mean one thing," Lazear declared. "What did she look like?"

"I have pictures to prove any extravagant claims," the Major said cautiously. "But she looked so good that three weeks later I wrote and said that I was going to join the army medical corps and then get married. After one visit! If my own son ever pulled such a trick, I'd say he had lost his mind. But it worked. I think Emilie was just surprised into it. If she had known *what* she was getting into!" He raised his eyebrows eloquently.

"About ten days before the scheduled date of the wedding, I was ordered to a new post in Arizona. Arizona! You young men wouldn't know about Arizona twenty years ago. Indian hunting-grounds and nothing more. My Miss Emilie Lawrence was an absolute genius when it came to doing needlepoint and looking pretty at the parlor piano. But how would she feel about being dragged three thousand miles to set up housekeeping in a tent? I even went to Washington to try and make the old Surgeon-General guarantee me some leave, but he didn't seem to think much of the idea! Finally I sent Emilie a telegram and told her to get ready for a wedding the next day. So she did, and next thing she knew, she was on her way to Arizona. What a woman! This 'weaker sex' line is as inaccurate as it's hackneyed."

"How long were you out there?" Lazear asked.

"Eighteen years. It's quite a way to practice medicine, really. The post doctor is the only doctor for hundreds of miles around, you know. I suppose I treated every disease in the books, and I'm sure I saw some that the books had never heard of. And surgery!" He shook his head, amazed at his recollections.

"How did you manage to get back East?" Agramonte asked.

"All the time I was out West, I had a friend in civilization who sent me all the medical journals he could get his hands on. I was afraid of losing touch with medical progress and ending up as nothing but a rural bone-setter. It was the articles on the new developments in bacteriology that nearly drove me crazy. Finally I couldn't stand it any more. I requested a transfer East to go to Johns Hopkins and study. Something must have slipped up somewhere along the line, because the transfer went through. And so here I am swatting bugs in Cuba."

Before the other men could ask any further questions, Reed looked at his watch. "I guess it's time to call it a night, gentlemen. Tomorrow should be a fairly tough day."

As they were leaving the building, Agramonte suddenly said, "Do I understand, Major, that you actually persuaded this lady to cut out the last two weeks of fussing over her wedding just by sending her a *telegram*?"

Reed looked surprised. "Why—yes," he answered. "Why do you ask?"

"I was just thinking," Agramonte said, "that if you've made up your mind to break this yellow-jack business, I don't suppose anything can stop you."

Salmonella icteroides proved to be a fluke. Cultures from eighteen living and eleven dead yellow-fever patients were studied by each of the four scientists. Not a trace of the bacillus could be found. It was checked off the list once and for all.

Even before the preliminary work was over, one of those happy accidents occurred which keep popping up in medical-research history to eliminate a day's work here and ten years' work there. At the Pinar del Rio barracks, a hundred miles from Havana, some sort of tropical-fever disease was raging. Yellow fever? No one was quite sure. Neither the commandant nor the post doctor of Pinar del Rio was noted for his efficiency. Reed and Agramonte went over, talked to the authorities, did a few autopsies, and took a long look around.

Reed had strange conclusions to report to his colleagues the next day. "Thirty-five of them are in the hospital," he said. "Eleven dead. All unmistakable cases." He looked to Agramonte for confirmation. Agramonte, as a native Cuban, had seen a lot of yellow fever. He nodded. Yellow fever was not hard to diagnose. There were only too many classic symptoms: frightful pains in the arms and legs; jaundice; the hemorrhages in the stomach which gave the disease its native name—*el vomito negro;* fever and delirium; and, usually, the delirious death. "Unmistakable cases," Reed repeated. "But does the post hospital know it? Oh, no." He raised his eyes eloquently. " 'Remittent malarial fever,' it says on the charts. Malarial fever!"

"But it made it so nice for us," Agramonte suggested pleasantly.

"It did," Reed admitted. "In principle it's a shocking boner, but in practice it worked out well. Because of it no one at the hospital paid any attention to the bedding of those men. There was no special disinfecting of their sheets, their mattresses, or their clothing. But——" He paused emphatically, "did any of the nurses, or the people in the laundry, or the other patients pick up yellow jack from the stuff? Not one. And the men in the barracks. Eight barracks were full of contaminated clothes. But no one—not one single man in any of those eight—caught anything."

"Don't forget the nervous sergeant," Agramonte put in.

"Oh, yes. The bunk of one of the men who died was taken over by a sergeant the night after it was vacated.

Of course he didn't know at the time that he was sleeping in what should have been a hotbed of yellow-fever germs. He didn't like it much when he found out either. But he was in perfectly good health the last time we saw him."

"*Fomites*——" Dr. Lazear said quizzically. Dr. Lazear had his own theory about yellow fever, and *fomites* were no part of it.

"Yes. Lots of *fomites.* That stuff should have had enough yellow jack in it to infect anyone who came within ten feet. Only it didn't. Here's another thing. There were eight men in the guardhouse. They'd been there for weeks. Hadn't been near the town or the hospital, to the best knowledge of the guards. Well, one of them died of yellow fever about two weeks ago. Just one. The others didn't have so much as a chill, not even the fellow who slept in the dead man's bunk after he'd been carried out of it."

Agramonte asked excitedly, "And why not? Whatever source of infection the yellow-fever victim was exposed to, the others must have been exposed to."

"They weren't immunes?" Carroll inquired cautiously.

"No. None of them has had it before. The question is, why haven't they got it now? And where did it come from in the first place?"

"There's an old man on this island," Lazear said, "who would tell you that it flew in the window on the wings of a female mosquito."

"Old Finlay?" Reed asked. "He's been saying it for quite a while, hasn't he?"

"In Cuba," Agramonte said, "it's hard to remember a time when old Finlay *wasn't* saying it."

The mosquito . . . Through all the controversy between the advocates of the *fomites* theory and the direct-contagion proponents, an old doctor with mutton-chop whiskers and the contradictory name of Carlos Finlay was holding out for the mosquito. He had been living in Havana for thirty-six years before the Yellow-Fever Commission arrived there, and for nineteen of them he had been trying to convince people that mosquitoes and nothing else transmitted yellow fever. He had never lost faith in the idea and had never stopped trying to prove it.

Dr. Finlay's theory carried little weight in medical circles. The mosquito? Could that ubiquitous little creature, annoying, but so harmless in appearance, really be the villain in so serious a plot? Ridiculous!

"How do the people down here feel about Finlay's ideas?" Reed asked after a few seconds' meditation.

"No one pays any attention to him any more," Agramonte said, "except the Father Superior of the Jesuits. He seems to think Finlay has something, and all the Jesuit houses on the island have regulations about mosquito control. Now, come to think of it, I haven't treated any of the priests for yellow fever as long as I can remember. An odd coincidence, isn't it?"

Reed said suddenly, "Did any of you ever read a

paper by an army surgeon named Henry Carter? About yellow-fever transmission?"

"Lord, yes," Lazear said. "We have it in our files. Trying to figure out Carter's figures is one of our favorite indoor sports. Let me get it out for you."

Henry Carter, stationed in Mississippi during a mild epidemic of yellow fever, had recorded some interesting observations about the strange behavior of yellow fever during the early stages of an epidemic. There was, he said, an unexplained time lapse between the first reported case and the resultant outbreak. Two or three weeks might pass before a second person developed any symptoms of the disease. But after that a rash of victims would be stricken all at once. The Commission went over its own statistics and found that they agreed with Dr. Carter's: one case, deceptive peace for about two weeks, then havoc. This state of affairs strongly suggested what the bacteriologists called "an intermediate host." Suppose that a yellow-fever victim—just one—is brought into town, on a ship, for example. Suppose that a passing mosquito bites the victim, thus drawing into her stomach the yellow-fever germ. Suppose that the germ incubates and is conveyed some days later to the salivary glands of the mosquito. From here on, everyone the mosquito bites is liable to the disease.

It now became abundantly clear that the claims of Dr. Finlay were due for some first-class investigation. Dr. Finlay himself was pleased but not surprised that the Commission had finally got around to calling on him. Never, he knew, had he expounded his favorite subject to a more important audience. Reed and his associates left, carrying Dr. Finlay's good wishes, all his collected literature on transmission by mosquito in other diseases (such as malaria), and a bowlful of mosquito eggs which he was cultivating. The Commissioners incubated and hatched these eggs into a fine collection of mosquitoes. The *Stegomyia fasciata* (now called *Aëdes aegypti*) Dr. Finlay believed to be the guilty species—specifically, the female.

"A pretty creature," Finlay had said, almost lovingly. "She has delicate wings and long silvery stripes on her body. And she's a timid, domestic lady–not a wanderer like the malaria-bearing *Anopheles*. She likes to stay in the same place, and once she's inside a house she stays there until driven out or killed. But she is not particular at all when it comes to breeding conditions. Any convenient spot will do: a poorly drained roof, a gutter, an empty flower-pot left out in the rain." Her lack of discrimination in this respect would be quite a problem.

Experiments with mosquitoes presented an unpleasant difficulty. Yellow fever, as far as the Commission knew, was a human disease. So far it had been impossible to infect laboratory animals. (Not until years after the Commission had disbanded would this be done.) Agramonte, the pathologist, had been trying for months to find a susceptible laboratory animal, but he had not succeeded.

Now proving the mosquito-transmission theory was, in principle, a simple matter. One would simply allow a mosquito to bite a yellow-fever victim, have the same mosquito bite a healthy man, and then sit back and wait for him to get yellow fever. But how could any man, especially the gentle, sympathetic Reed, take such a responsibility with human life? It was his business to save lives, not to sacrifice them by trying to prove an idea that an old man had dreamed up nineteen years ago and hadn't yet demonstrated satisfactorily.

The other three were less tender-hearted. Hundreds of thousands of people, they pointed out, had already died of yellow fever. What difference did it make if a few more got it or even died of it, if by doing so they could put an end to the business once and for all? In the recent war with Spain, only 862 men had been killed in battle, and 106 had died of wounds. But 5,438 people had died of disease—typhoid and yellow fever leading the list.

All this made sense, but it did not bring about Reed's decision to use human guinea pigs. The clinching argument was that yellow fever could not, at the time, be produced in animals. Therefore human beings must be infected with it. No matter how delicate the conscience of a researcher, he could arrive at no other conclusion. Volunteers would have to be called for, but the first volunteers, the Commission decided, would be the Commission itself.

While they were making their initial plans, Reed had to return to the States on medical business. He promised to return as quickly as possible, leaving his three colleagues to begin Operation Mosquito.

The insects, hatched from the eggs presented by Finlay, had fed, one by one, on the blood of yellow-fever patients at the Las Animas yellow-fever ward in Havana. Lazear, a mosquito expert, had charge of the brood. He kept each of them in its own gauze-stoppered jar, each jar labeled with the date on which the mosquito had bitten a patient and the stage of the disease at the time.

Lazear and Carroll quietly corralled a few volunteers. They were not sure that what they were doing was legal, and with the head of the Commission away, they decided to avoid needless gossip. Dr. Lazear made the first experiment on himself and some of his friends. Agramonte, to his own annoyance, was immune, having had the disease in childhood. The technique was simple. One lured the mosquito into a test-tube, inverted the tube over the arm, tapped the bottom of the glass to call the attention of the creature to the treat at the other end, and let her bite. That was all there was to it.

To Dr. Lazear's disgust, no one got yellow fever. Could they be naturally immune? Or had his mosquitoes been too recently infected to pass along the disease? He wondered. On August 27th he took Dr. Carroll into the laboratory and showed him a mosquito which he considered the prize of his collection. This insect had bitten not one but four yellow-fever patients, the first of them twelve days ago. The cases had ranged from very mild to very severe. If any mosquito of his brood was ripe for action, Lazear asserted, this was it.

"Let's give her a chance to show off," Carroll said, observing the innocent-looking insect curiously through his rimless glasses.

Lazear's handsome face was solemn. "You're sure you want to try?"

"Didn't you?"

Lazear smiled. "And what happened? Nothing."

"Well, better luck next time. Here. Let her out." Carroll rolled up his sleeves and thoughtfully watched the mosquito as she slid down the tube and lighted on his arm. The night after, he wrote to Reed. "If there is anything in the mosquito theory," he said, "I should get a good dose."

He did. For three days his recovery was a matter of doubtful conjecture. Lazear was frantic with worry. Of course he had done what he set out to do. He had produced the first experimental case of yellow fever by the bite of a mosquito. But had he killed his friend in the process? Almost, but not quite. Slowly Carroll began to rally, and soon he was out of danger.

Their fears at rest, Lazear and Agramonte considered the situation objectively. Carroll's yellow fever showed that they were on the right track. Soon Carroll himself was in a position to appreciate his own illness. As soon as he had enough strength to read, he began poring over his chart and studying the lab reports which Lazear had kept so carefully. Recorded on the chart was a notation in the handwriting of his nurse, who had written, "Says he got his illness through the bite of a mosquito—delirious!"

Lazear, Agramonte, and Carroll, conferring at the latter's bedside, were jubilant. Further success had come to them from the mosquito. Lazear had allowed her to bite another volunteer, obliquely referred to in their reports as Case XY (actually a young private named William Dean.) Case XY also contracted the disease, but he threw it off with less difficulty than the forty-six-year-old Carroll had done.

Two cases of mosquito-transmission! . . . Lazear's heart was filled with strange affection for his brood. Reed would be back soon and then things would really start popping! The young man's head was buzzing with ideas for procedure and practice. He was more sure than any of them that they would soon see their theory turned into undeniable fact. A week later he was dead of one of the worst yellow-fever cases the hospital had ever seen.

When Reed returned in October, he found the shadow of his colleague's fate lying heavily over the camp. He himself was so saddened by the tragedy that even the promised success of their mission could produce no emotion in him at all. How had it happened, he asked. There was unanimous agreement that it had been an accident.

What kind of accident?

"A mosquito bit him while he was making the ward rounds," Carroll said. "He says he noticed it, but he didn't think it was the right kind of a mosquito and he let it stay on his hand. He told me about it the day he got sick. He even told Major Gorgas when he came to see him."

He had, it developed, told quite a few people about it. Reed wondered. Lazear, the mosquito expert, in doubt about the identification of the species? Lazear, who had been the most enthusiastic in the adoption of the Finlay theory, carelessly allowing a stray mosquito to remain on him in a yellow-fever ward?

It seemed impossible, yet it had really happened. Lazear himself had told the story—Lazear who had a wife, two small children, and nothing in the world for them except his job and an insurance policy. . . . Had the imminence of Carroll's death awakened him to the fearful responsibility he was taking with his own life? If he had had some sort of premonition, it had been only too accurate. His death was officially declared by the Commission to be an accident. That was the least they could do for him.

Their first enthusiasm gone, Reed, Carroll and

Agramonte got back to work. They had two cases to work with, but one of them, Carroll's, was not considered conclusive by anyone but himself. He had, after all, been exposed to all the yellow fever in the Las Animas hospital for weeks. How did anyone know that the mosquito bite had anything to do with his attack? Logicians would make short work of such a claim.

But Mr. XY was something else again. He had been in the hospital at Camp Columbia for two months, and there was no yellow fever at Camp Columbia. Lazear's mosquito had been the only source of infection to which he had been exposed. On the basis of his present knowledge, Reed took two decisive steps. He wrote a paper to be read at an American Health Association meeting in which he stated categorically: "The mosquito acts as the intermediate host for the parasite of yellow fever." And he applied to the Military Governor of Cuba for an appropriation large enough to carry out one large-scale piece of research, so perfectly controlled that not even the most violent anti-mosquito, pro-*fomites* men could quarrel with the results.

This was the origin of Camp Lazear, which became the official testing ground of the commission. While the station was in the planning stages, Reed worried over one vital point. Since Lazear's death and Carroll's near escape, the work of the Commission, taken lightly at first, had been regarded with greater and greater awe by the American soldiers and the natives alike.

The experimental station would soon be ready, but would there be anyone around on whom to experiment? Reed himself was the only member of the board left who was not immune. He was anxious to try one of the mosquitoes on himself, but it was not practical to do so until he was sure that operations at the camp were running smoothly. Fifty-year-old men, he knew, did not make quick recoveries from yellow fever, assuming that they recovered at all. The Military Governor of Cuba, General Wood, had promised appropriations large enough to pay volunteers for their services, and this information was spread through the barracks and among the native population.

The day after the news made the rounds of Camp Columbia, Reed was visited in his office by two young men named John Moran and John Kissinger. They had heard about the Major's need for volunteers in the yellow-fever tests, they said. They would be willing to help out.

Reed was amazed. These two men, about the age of his own son, were hospital corpsmen. They knew yellow fever. He said, "I admire your courage, boys. I know that you both understand exactly what you're letting yourselves in for." They nodded. "In any case, I'm glad that we have appropriations to compensate you for your services. It's not much, considering. But—one hundred dollars if you don't get yellow jack; two hundred if you do. We——"

"Major," Moran interrupted, "we weren't figuring on anything like that. In fact," he added more decisively, "we wouldn't want to do it if we had to take money for it."

This time Reed was really taken aback. He said, "But you—suppose that——" He stopped and studied their faces briefly. "Are you sure that's the way you feel about it?"

"Yes sir," Kissinger said. "We don't care about the money. But we thought that——" He flushed slightly. "We thought we'd like to do something for humanity and science." Moran nodded, solemn-faced.

Reed sighed, touched both by their spirit and by the naive expression of it. He said simply, "Gentlemen, I salute you." Of these two he wrote later, "In my opinion, this exhibition of moral courage has never been surpassed in the annals of the United States Army."

Camp Lazear was not much except an open field on which seven tents were pitched and two small houses were built. The permanent personnel housed by this unlikely post numbered fifteen. Three of them were the remaining members of the Commission; three more were staff men known to be immune to yellow fever. They represented the link between Camp Lazear and the outside world which, although it was only one mile away, might just as well have been a thousand miles off for all the other residents of the camp saw of it. From the day of its unceremonious opening, the experimental station was under strict quarantine. No one could come into it but its immune members; its nonimmune members could leave it whenever they cared to, but once they went out they could never return. All the people inside were known to be free from yellow-fever infection at the time the experiments began. Nor were there any mosquitoes on the well-drained, windy field except the specially bred laboratory insects trapped in the Commission's test-tubes. As of December 5, 1900 at two o'clock in the afternoon, Camp Lazear was the one spot in Cuba absolutely guaranteed to be safe from yellow fever.

Agramonte, stationed at the yellow-fever hospital in Havana, was in charge of mosquito-infecting. He had an inexhaustible source of supply. In the Las Animas ward there were men in every possible stage of the disease. Agramonte himself transferred the insects from the hospital to the camp, his pockets bulging with test-tubes. Once in camp, the bugs were removed to artificially warmed quarters, were coddled and catered to as no mosquitoes in history had ever before been pampered.

Kissinger was the first of the volunteers to be bitten, his partner in the experiment a mosquito which had sucked the blood of a yellow-fever patient eleven days before. The camp waited, no one more eagerly than Kissinger, for the incubation period to pass. The camp noted, no one more regretfully than Kissinger, that he remained in roaring good health. A second try, with the same mosquito, produced no results whatsoever on Kissinger. The mosquito herself died three days later.

"What do you think it is, Major?" the soldier asked him one day, after a quick check had shown his pulse to be seventy-two, his temperature 98.6, and his blood pressure 120. "Is it me or the mosquitoes? It must be me. I'm probably immune." Kissinger had allied himself strongly on the side of the mosquito-transmission theory, largely through his growing devotion to Reed.

"Not necessarily. We have a new idea on the incubation period required now that the weather's colder. Let's try it again. This time we'll really do the job right. Five mosquitoes—they all bit yellow-fever cases over two weeks ago."

"Anything you say, Major," the boy agreed, grinning broadly. He added hopefully, "Wait and see! I'll get yellow jack this time if it kills me!"

Reed winced imperceptibly. It had not been the happiest choice of words.

Three days later, Kissinger was exhibiting all the symptoms of yellow fever. He was removed to the Las Animas hospital and every local yellow-fever authority, actual and self-appointed, was invited to come in and look at him.

It was a good case—unmistakably yellow fever, but mild enough to make recovery certain. It was all that the camp could have asked. None of the visiting physicians disputed the diagnosis. And no one was happier to see a man stricken with yellow fever than old Carlos Finlay. This was the day for which he had waited nineteen years.

While Kissinger had been waiting to be stricken, another sort of experiment was under way at the camp. Proving that the female *Aëdes aegypti* spread yellow fever was only half the job. Proving that the traditional *fomites* did not transmit the disease was the other half. Orders passed from Reed to the Las Animas hospital, and some days later three mysterious wooden boxes were delivered to the camp and deposited in one of the small houses which had been built at Camp Lazear by the engineering corps.

It was an ugly little shack, fourteen by twenty feet in size, its walls two boards thick, its heavily-screened windows shuttered and guaranteed to prevent good ventilation. A double-doored vestibule admitted one to this unpleasant little home which came equipped with a coal-oil stove and a temperature of ninety degrees. Building Number One, as it was called, contained nothing but the stove, three army cots, and now the contributions from Las Animas. A volunteer doctor and two hospital-corps privates went into the house and broke open the crates.

Many brave men have taken desperate chances with their lives to prove a scientific point. With the danger there is usually a touch of the odd excitement, verging on exhilaration, which accompanies danger undergone for a "cause." The aura which surrounds such danger is often sufficient compensation for the risk.

For these three heroes there was no such consolation. The experiments performed in Building Number One at Camp Lazear surely stand unchallenged as the most unlovely scientific experiments in history. "The greatest exhibition of moral courage in the annals of the United States Army"? Camp Lazear was breaking all records.

For two weeks the boxes had been packed tight with soiled linen and blankets from the yellow-fever hospital. Special pains had been taken in the packing of these boxes. Not just ordinarily dirty linen passed the rigid examination. These sheets had to be stiff with the black effluvium which gave the disease its popular name, *el vomito negro.*

The three men dumped the contents of the boxes onto the floor, then shook out each object thoroughly, in order to "spread" the yellow fever with which the mess was supposed to be loaded. The first shock was too much for them and, to a man, they dashed for the door of the horrible little house, gasping for fresh air. The impulse to shake the dust of Camp Lazear from their feet must, at that moment, have been as overpowering as the atmosphere of Building Number One. But they went back inside. They had volunteered for the *fomites* experiment and they would stay with it. And if any *fomites* in the world could produce yellow fever, these were the *fomites* to do it.

They made up the beds with the linen and blankets,

crawled in between the sheets and waited for morning. It is not to be supposed that they slept. Next morning they were conducted to the quarantined tent where they were to spend their days for the duration of the experiment.

This was on November 30th. Until December 19th, twenty-one days later, the three men returned to their reeking house with each sunset and stayed there until morning.

"Hey, fellows," the immune soldier who brought them their food announced one day. "Kissinger has yellow jack—from a mosquito. He's been sent to Las Animas."

One of the inmates looked bored. "Private Kissinger," he announced to his companions, ceremoniously turning to address them, "has yellow jack—from a mosquito."

"Poor fellow. Imagine having to go to that nice clean hospital," one of the others said, clucking sympathetically. "Do extend our good wishes to Private Kissinger and tell him that if he can think of any way in which we could replace him, we would be only too happy."

"Well, after all," the messenger said, somewhat taken aback, "if mosquitoes *do* spread yellow fever, then maybe *fomites* don't, and you fellows are safe."

"At this point, son, a nice case of yellow fever would be a pleasure, an absolute joy," the first private announced pleasantly.

"But——"

"You wouldn't understand. Pass along, old friend, and don't disturb our thoughts. We only have twenty-four hours a day to think, you know."

On December 19th the three heroes were released from further dealings with *fomites* and were observed under quarantine for five days. After that they were allowed the run of the camp, not a flushed face or a racing pulse among them.

Two more volunteers took up nightly residence in Building Number One, under similar conditions, but with an added touch. These men wore the very pyjamas that had belonged to yellow-fever victims. And twenty days later they were succeeded by two others who slept on pillow cases soaked in the blood of assorted yellow-fever victims.

Of the whole experiment Reed wrote simply, "The attempt which we have made to infect Building Number One and its seven nonimmune occupants during a period of sixty-three days has proved an absolute failure." What the seven nonimmune occupants might have said to anyone who ever suggested to them afterwards that *fomites* convey yellow fever would probably make stimulating reading.

The second house at Camp Lazear was similar to Building Number One in size, but in no other way. It was well ventilated; it was furnished with nothing but steam-disinfected articles; its bedding was sterile; its residents were sent in fresh from long, soapy baths.

It was the sort of place that must have haunted the dreams of the men who were living in Building Number One.

Building Number Two was divided in the middle by a sheet of fine wire net, but its windows were arranged to insure good cross-ventilation. Into one side of the building were released fifteen hungry mosquitoes. Shortly after, they were joined by John Moran, the second of Reed's first two volunteers. At the same time, two other nonimmunes entered the other side of the house and watched through the mosquito-proof wire while the more discerning of the fifteen mosquitoes went to work on Private Moran. Three times that day, Moran return to the house for the purpose of being bitten by the contaminated insects. Four days later—on Christmas day, specifically—Moran had a fever of 104.2°. The other occupants of the building remained in excellent health.

The filthy, reeking houseful of *fomites* had done no harm to anyone. In the antiseptic dwelling next door, a man had caught yellow fever. The case was proved beyond the shadow of a doubt.

These clean-cut experiments, backed by the authority of the United States Army, brought about the acceptance of the Commission's findings by the rest of the profession more quickly than most revolutions in thought are accepted. Research experts had produced the facts. It was up to another group of experts to make use of them. The yellow-fever fight entered its second stage under the aegis of the Havana Sanitation Department.

The chief of the department was Major William Gorgas, later to be the Surgeon-General of the army. As a sanitation expert Gorgas was well known in the city long before the Yellow Fever Commission arrived. Although he had been opposed to the theory of mosquito transmission until the days of Camp Lazear, he himself had made an important contribution to the fund of knowledge with which the commission had gone to work. He had absolutely disproved the time-honored belief that yellow fever thrives in dirty surroundings. Havana was a hotbed of yellow fever, but Havana was probably the cleanest city in the world. Whatever city had had William Gorgas as its chief sanitation officer would have been kept clean. Once the findings of the Commission were made public, the Sanitation Department had no doubts about its proper procedure. The full power of the Medical Corps was turned full-blast against the female *Stegomyia* mosquito. She was doomed by act of Congress.

It was impossible, the natives said. There had always been mosquitoes. There would always be mosquitoes.

"Undoubtedly," Major Gorgas thought. "But with a little careful strategy they can be made harmless."

The first step in the campaign was the careful segregation of all current cases of yellow fever, and the first battalion of doomed mosquitoes were those found in the immediate area. The female *Stegomyia,* the sanitation squad was reminded, is a home-lover. She could easily be trapped on the premises, once she was there, or prevented from entering by means of fine screening. Sanitation officers went on duty, working eight-hour shifts, in every house and hospital on the island which contained a yellow-fever patient. Their duties were simple and clear-cut: keep the mosquitoes away from the patient.

This frontal attack cut off the supplies of infection at their source. Other measures followed. The hunted insect was sought out in every hiding-place she could find. No obscure rain-barrel, neglected roof-gutter, or out-of-the-way drain pipe could escape the eye of the fanatical Sanitation Corps. Eggs were destroyed almost as soon as they were laid. Larvae were slaughtered before they developed wings. The city reeked of kerosene, insect powder, and sulphur fumes. By September of 1901 there was not a single case of yellow fever left in Havana.

The double accomplishment of Reed and Gorgas was soon tried out on a large scale. Plans were being made for the greatest chore of engineering which the United States had ever attempted: the construction of a shipping canal across the fever-ridden jungles of Central America. It was no secret to anyone concerned that the job would be impossible unless some sort of fever control could be set up. There were simply not enough foolhardy men available.

Gorgas was a natural choice for the job of Sanitation

Officer. The heartbreaking struggle to control yellow fever in this miasmal death-trap was fought for a long time against odds too great even for his peculiar genius. But in the end he won out over the mosquito, and he stands as high as Goethals, the engineer, in the ranks of those who built the Panama Canal.

The yellow-fever picture is complete now. The elusive filterable virus, after many false alarms, has been identified; the vaccine to counteract it has been developed; the probable source of all the epidemics—yellow fever in animals—has been discovered in the jungles of South America. In its entirety, the yellow-fever story represents a great triumph of man over nature. But whenever the human race becomes obsessed with its own cleverness, it might remind itself that four hundred years, thousands of lives, millions of dollars, a rare collection of scientific brilliance, the United States Army, and the big stick of Teddy Roosevelt were required before men could get ahead of the mosquito.

part IV

New Miracles for the New Century

7

The Discovery of Insulin

DR. FREDERICK BANTing, an instructor in physiology at the University of Western Ontario, did most of the preparation for his classroom lectures during his evening office hours. Early in his practice he had discovered that this was a convenient time to work. He was sure to be alone.

When he felt gloomy enough to brood, as he frequently did, the young man considered the paradox of his two careers. He was by training and inclination an orthopedic surgeon, but he had practically no patients. By no standard was he a trained physiologist, yet he was in sole charge of a class of eager physiology students. He had, it seemed to him, managed his life with marvelous consistency. At the age of twenty-eight he was a failure in everything.

As he sat correcting quiz papers in his unattractive little office on the poorer side of town, the young doctor frequently wondered what had ever possessed him to study medicine in the first place.

Certainly he had not inherited a taste for it. The Bantings of Alliston had been farmers for generations. Within the memory of all living Bantings, no member of the family had ever gone beyond high school, and young Fred's departure for Toronto's Victoria College had been a topic of some interest to Alliston society, which had not expected too much of the youngest Banting. Fred had been a pleasant, undistinguished boy. He had done neither well nor badly in school. When he enrolled in the University of Toronto Medical School in 1911, no one dreamed that soon the name Banting would be one of the most illustrious in the university's history.

Fred Banting's calculations were upset by the first World War, which overtook him exactly halfway through his course. The class of '17 (it accelerated to graduate in 1916) enlisted in the Canadian Army as a unit, and Banting found himself a doctor and a captain on the same day. Three years later he was back in Alliston with a healed wound, a gold medal for heroism in action, and no job.

He was nearly twenty-eight; he had been unofficially engaged for nearly ten years; and he had not even begun his internship. Although he had always felt himself drawn to research, Banting realized that it was an uncertain way for a family man to make a living. Now surgery was something else again. And both his army and his college experience suggested that he might have a flair for the art.

He spent the next year in the Toronto Children's Hospital, and then looked around for a strategic place to open an office. London, Ontario, was a pleasant town, not far from Toronto. Its small university offered him a reasonably paid six-hour course in orthopedic surgery to teach, and full moral support in the establishment of a practice. In July of 1920 he packed his worldly possessions into a battered but highly esteemed Ford and set off for his new home.

By September of the same year, he was easily the most unhappy man in the province of Ontario, and probably the most discouraged in the whole of Canada. It seemed impossible to him to build up a practice. Fred was a good surgeon, but he was a *new* surgeon. To the sixty thousand citizens of London, it seemed that he might as well have been an apprentice butcher. After twelve weeks of practice, he found that he was averaging about four dollars a month. He had already borrowed heavily to make the down payment on the house, now heavily mortgaged, which he had bought in the belief that he was soon to be married. But that was another plan which had not worked out according to schedule.

Although Banting had been decorated for heroism under fire during the war, he was almost painfully unsure of himself in the more complex field of human relations. It was typical of his nature that he had believed in waiting until he would be well established before marrying. But after ten years his fiancée greeted each new postponement with increasing coolness. Soon a rival with a flourishing business appeared on the scene, and Banting sadly found himself a free man.

Free was the word to describe him. He had no wife, no patients, and only six hours of teaching with which to fill out the week. The heartsickness of those days demanded immediate distraction. Banting took up painting and began to look around for an extra job.

"Listen, Fred," a sympathetic colleague told him one day, "there's a vacancy in the physiology department—they had to split one section and there's no one in the department with any free hours. Why don't you go to see Miller and apply for the job?"

"Physiology! All I know about physiology I learned in one required course about seven years ago!"

"You need a job, don't you?"

"Certainly I need a job, but——"

"Can't you put up a bluff? Tell Miller you took some graduate work in England, or something. You're already on the faculty, so nobody will check up on you."

Banting smiled. "I'll tell him *something* persuasive," he said.

He went up to the department office and rapped boldly on the door.

"Dr. Miller?"

"Hello, Dr. Banting. How are you? What can we do for you up here?"

"I understand you have a vacancy on the staff."

The doctor raised his eyebrows eloquently. "Have we! Biggest enrollment I've ever seen. Have you a friend who's interested?"

"*I'm* interested."

"You! What's the matter?" The older man smiled. "Have you perfected orthopedic surgery to the point of boredom?"

"No. But I'd love to take up physiology too."

"Good enough! You've done post-graduate work, I suppose?"

"No—right out of school and into the army. Then internship, and here I am. Not an hour of post-graduate work."

"I see—I suppose you've kept up your interest on the side—read the new literature, and——"

"Dr. Miller," Banting said somberly, "I have been interested in physiology for quite a few years, but I haven't got around to it very often. I want this job because I need money in the worst way. I have no qualifications at all, but I can easily keep a few chapters ahead of the class because I have so much free time. I have free time because I have so few patients. That's why I need the money. It all ties in."

Dr. Miller opened his mouth, closed it, then roared with laughter. "Banting," he said, when he could speak, "if our vocational director could hear your technique of job application, it would take a year off his life. In the absence of any applicant more qualified, I hereby appoint you to the staff of the department of physiology. And to repay you for your frankness, I might as well tell you that you are, to date, the *only* applicant." He stood up and extended his hand. Banting shook it, grinning broadly. Officially, he was now a physiologist.

He took his new job seriously. Keeping ahead of the sophomores was a job which sharply reduced the number of hours available for brooding. He soon became almost a permanent fixture in the little T-shaped library of the medical school, where he plugged away at each lecture with iron determination, secretly suspecting that his students knew more than he did. At night he simply removed the necessary books to his office and went on working there. It was late in October that he encountered the knottiest problem in the course.

As he sat chewing meditatively on a pencil and considering a dog-eared page of the book, there was a rap on the screen. "A patient?" he thought. "It can't be!"

He jumped up and rushed to the outer office. A small boy, his nearest neighbor, stood outside, brandishing a finger in an accusing manner. "Oh, hello, Billy," Banting said. "I thought you were a patient."

"I *am* a patient," the boy announced, entering the room unceremoniously.

"What's your trouble?"

"Splinter."

"Where?"

"Finger."

"How?"

"Sliding for third base. Mom says you should take it out, and I should give you this." He presented a small bag which proved to be filled with homemade biscuits. Such payments, Banting realized, were more practical than an I.O.U.

"They look good. Come on in and let me see that finger. How'd the game come out?"

"Oh, we lost," the patient announced airily. "Our best pitcher is home sick with something."

"Too bad. Sit here under the light." He fished a pair of tweezers from his sterilizer and then soaked a piece of cotton in alcohol.

"What were *you* doing?" the boy asked, frowning suspiciously at the stack of books on Banting's desk.

"Studying."

"Why do *you* have to study? You're a doctor!"

"You always have to study, no matter who you are." Banting extracted the splinter so quickly that the patient barely had time to wince.

"What are you studying?"

"The effects of the pancreas on carbohydrate metabolism."

"What's that?"

"What's the difference?"

"I want to know!"

This was a week end. It had been Banting's custom to visit out of town every week end, and his associations with the past now made the house on Adelaide Street three times as gloomy on Saturday as it was on Monday. He suddenly realized that company of any description was exactly what he had been hoping for all evening.

"Well, it's easy," he said. "Carbohydrate metabolism is the study of how the body uses starches and sugars for energy."

"Is that all?"

Banting smiled. "Wouldn't it be nice if that *were* all? No. There's a lot more. What I'm fussing about tonight is the way the pancreas influences this carbohydrate metabolism."

"What's the pancreas?"

"Did you ever eat sweetbreads?"

"Once. That was enough!"

"Sweetbreads are the pancreases of calves. The human pancreas is a small—— Here, I'll show you." He reached for the book and flipped through it until he had found a diagram of the digestive organs. "See?"

He tapped a finger against the small, oblong organ

lying just behind the stomach. "Now this thing has two kinds of cells in it. Do you know what cells are?"

The boy smiled indulgently. "We had that two years ago in school," he announced.

"Oh. Sorry. Well, the pancreas has two kinds—outer and inner. The outer cells are connected to the digestive system by tubes—ducts, they're called. They produce enzymes—digestive juices, you know—called trypsin, amylopsin, and lipase, of all things! The ducts carry the juices into the digestive tract. But I'm not worrying about them just now. It's the inner cells!" He raised a disapproving eyebrow.

"What's their trouble?" the boy inquired suspiciously.

"I'm coming to it. They have no ducts, by the way, so they just pour their juices into the blood stream by a direct route."

"Juices with silly names like the others?"

"Ah, no! The outer cells do all that heavy work. The secretion of the inner cell is something very special. Quite delicate in fact. But let's not get ahead of ourselves. Let's start with—oh, with one of these biscuits." He seized one, ate it in one swallow, and said, "There. That's starch—darn good, I might add. Don't forget to tell your mother. Now, when the carbohydrate in that biscuit gets down into the intestines, all the digestive juices go to work and change it into a very simple form of sugar called glucose. Got that?"

"Maybe I'd follow it better if *I* had some starch too."

"A good point." Banting pulled out a second biscuit and gave it to him. "Now this glucose is pretty valuable stuff. As soon as it's made, it's picked up by the blood stream and rushed, express collect, to the liver. That's the big three-piece organ to the right of the stomach. In the liver it's changed into something called glycogen."

"Called what?"

"Glycogen. There's a fancy name! The old-time doctors used to call it 'animal starch'—much more descriptive. It's stored in the liver until you need it."

"When's that?"

"That's the joke. It's always needed, in one amount or another. Whenever you need any energy—enough to hit a home run, enough to chew a biscuit, enough to breathe. In fact, whenever any muscle of the body wants to operate. Now when that happens—and remember that it's happening every minute, as long as you live—a most amazing series of events take place. But it all happens in just a flash of the time it takes me to tell you about it. Some of this glycogen is sent from the liver to the muscle that wants it. Then it's reconverted into its original form—glucose. It's united with oxygen from the lungs and burns up. Result? Energy is produced."

"You hit the home run?"

"Or chew the biscuit. Or just breathe. Of course, exactly how all this happens and just what comes before what, I don't know. No one does—yet." He allowed this cautious disclaimer to sink in, then continued. "Now there's one step in the process that I haven't mentioned. But what a step it is! While the glycogen is being rushed out of the liver, the secretion of the inner cells of the pancreas is also being carried to the acting muscle." He paused for breath.

"What does it do when it gets there?"

"Plenty. It's the 'spark' that sets off the burning of the glucose. Now if it *doesn't* arrive—if the inner cells of the pancreas are injured or suddenly aren't producing any secretion, the trouble starts. The 'unsparked' sugar accumulates first in the muscle, then in the blood. And the next thing you know, all your reserves of energy are gone, and you're in a bad way with diabetes, and then——"

"Diabetes! I know what that is."

"You do?"

"Sure. That's what Joe has."

"Joe?"

"He's our best pitcher," the boy explained. "I told you."

"Oh. How long has he had it?"

"About two months. He can't play any more, because he's too thin, I guess. He didn't come back to school yet, anyway. How long does it take to get over diabetes?"

"It—it depends."

"I mean do you think he'll be able to play by spring?"

He'll be dead by spring, Banting thought. He said, "I hope so."

There was a moment of silence. Banting felt his early-evening depression weighing on him heavily. The boy said, *"Then* what happens?"

"Oh, that's all. Only it's really more complicated than that. Maybe I'd better start studying again." He handed the boy a small plaster, and said, "Take that dressing off tomorrow, and put this on if the finger's sore. Otherwise, never mind."

"O.K." The boy stood up. "Tell me the rest some time."

"The rest? What rest?"

The boy laughed, amused by this evidence of density in his learned friend. "You didn't say what makes the inner cells stop working or how you start them working again."

"Oh." Banting opened the door. "Well, you go home, and I'll think about it." Not that there was any need to think, he said to himself. No one knew what made the inner cells stop working; there was no way to start them up again. That took care of both questions.

His students would ask the same basic questions, Banting knew, although their phrasing would be more complicated, befitting their dignity as sophomores. Actually he could not tell them much more than he had told the boy.

Diabetes? In 1920 diabetes was an incurable disease which could be treated by one method only: heroic dieting, actually near-starvation, which usually left its victims little interest in the life prolonged with such difficulty. The physician dreaded the disease almost as much as his patients did. It was a cruel illness to treat, and a terrible one to die of.

Although satisfactory treatment for diabetes was unknown in Banting's professional days, diabetes itself is one of the earliest diseases to appear in written history. There is no mistaking its identity in medical descriptions put down even 4000 years ago. When Aretaeus, a second-century physician of Cappadocia, wrote a famous clinical description of the disease, it had apparently been named for some time. "Diabetes is a wonderful affection," he said, "being a melting down of the flesh into urine . . . Life is painful and disgusting, thirst unquenchable, drinking excessive."

The trio of symptoms was as significant to physicians 750 years ago as it is today: rapid loss of weight; excessive urination, caused by the body's attempt to dissolve some of the excessive sugar; and unquenchable thirst, a distress signal set up to help combat the drastic loss of body fluid. The fourth characteristic could hardly be called a symptom, although it never failed to make its appearance with the other three. "Death is speedy," Aretaeus wrote. He might have added, "And inevitable."

Death *was* inevitable, following the "painful and disgusting" life of hunger, thirst, and exhaustion. Often the illness did not run its course; its victim became more liable to other fatal diseases: pneumonia, blood poisoning, gangrene. For children afflicted with diabetes, the most optimistic life expectancy was one year.

In the wave of brilliant research which followed the discoveries of Pasteur and Koch, diabetes had no part. Here there was no germ to look for, no vaccine to develop, no contagion to check. Diabetes does not come from the outside. It comes because a delicate mechanism inside the body, for reasons unknown even today, suddenly breaks down.

The pancreas was not known to be connected with diabetes until 1888, when the German scientist Naunyn began to study the problem. Although before his time almost every organ of the body, including the blood, had been suspected, Naunyn proved the responsibility of the pancreas beyond a shadow of doubt. His method was simple. He removed the pancreases of laboratory animals and found that without exception diabetes resulted. Naunyn and his colleagues showed early in the proceedings, however, that the three digestive juices, or enzymes, produced by the outer cells of the pancreas, had no connection with the disease. One could cut the ducts which connected these cells to the intestinal tract without producing a symptom of diabetes.

Twenty years before Naunyn's discovery, another German scientist named Paul Langerhans had found the second type of pancreatic cell—the internal cell that pours its secretion directly into the blood stream. When Langerhans' work was correlated with Naunyn's, the two interlocked neatly. Diabetes was caused by the failure of these "islets of Langerhans" to secrete their mysterious substance.

The problem of diabetes meant more to Banting than just a footnote to his lecture on the pancreas. He was a doctor first and an academic lecturer almost by accident. He had seen the disease at close quarters. Years ago he had watched it run its course in a beloved childhood friend. In medical school he had learned the stringent regulations of diet to be imposed on a diabetic patient. During his internship he had seen it in its cruelest form at the Children's Hospital. And since then, he had studied more than one case history in which death had come almost as a relief after a life burdened not only by near physical starvation, but by the resulting mental agony of intense preoccupation with the idea of food, particularly sugar.

Banting could predict, almost to the exact wording, one question which his students would ask him. If diabetes is caused by a failure of the pancreas to produce a necessary secretion, why not simply extract this secretion from animal pancreases and supply it to the patient artificially?

So obvious an idea had been thought of before, of course, but there was a catch to it. There were, in fact, three catches: trypsin, amylopsin, lipase—the three digestive juices secreted by the outer cells of the pancreas. These enzymes are powerful chemicals. Brought into contact with the delicate secretion of the internal cells, they destroy it. One could take out an animal pancreas easily enough, could grind it up, make a solution of its "extracts" and inject the solution into a diabetic patient, with two results: the injection would supply the patient with some unnecessary digestive juice; and the strong secretions would give him a skin boil, from which blood poisoning would probably develop.

Banting was vaguely aware that many distinguished research men had given their best efforts to this particular problem. It was not likely that a poorly prepared instructor in sophomore physiology could do anything about it no matter how much time he spent preparing for his classes. He gave what he considered a wholly inadequate lecture on the pancreas, and left it at that.

The subject came up again, quite by chance.

"Dr. Banting!" The librarian flagged his attention as he was making a noiseless exit from the library.

"Hmm?"

"Do you want to take this home tonight? I won't have to put it on the rack until morning." It was the November, 1920 issue of a magazine called *Surgery, Gynecology, and Obstetrics.*

"Thanks! I'll bring it in first thing in the morning," Banting said.

He tucked the fateful publication under his arm and went home. To his vast surprise, he had a patient waiting, and by the time he had worked through a set of test papers and had finally got around to the publication, he was reasonably tired. He opened the magazine tentatively and blinked in astonishment. The title of the very first article dispelled his fit of yawning as effectively as a cup of black coffee. His favorite subject turning up in a journal of surgery? He plunged into the article eagerly.

"The Relation of the Islets of Langerhans to Diabetes," it was called, with the traditional longwindedness of scientific titles, "with Special Reference to Causes of Pancreatic Lithiasis," by Dr. Moses Barron of Minneapolis.

Dr. Barron was an authority on lithiasas—stone formation—as Banting knew. His article described some curious cases which had come to his attention. Pancreatic stones had lodged not in the pancreas itself, but in the ducts which connect its outer cells to the intestinal tract. He reported that in every case blocking-off of the pancreatic ducts had been followed by a destruction of the external cells. The strong digestive juices, unable to escape, had collected in these cells, eventually destroying them.

Banting mused over the article for the duration of his office hours, then went upstairs to bed and fell asleep. Or almost. At the boundary of consciousness, he suddenly came fully awake, jumped out of bed, rushed to the desk, and wrote a note to himself.

When he woke up the next morning, he studied the

message thoughtfully. It was three sentences long, and it said: "Ligate the pancreatic ducts of dogs. Wait six to eight weeks for degeneration. Remove the residue and extract." That was all. Subconsciously primed for such a moment, his mind had evolved the complete solution of the problem. By tying off the ducts of the outer cells, one could make them dry up completely. If the outer cells were dried up, they could hardly go on secreting the strong digestive juices. And if the digestive juices were no longer in the pancreas, what would be left but the pure secretion of the internal cells?

But why had so simple a procedure not been carried out long ago? He sat down at his desk and studied the notation carefully. Where were the errors in his reasoning? What was the flaw in the method? The only objection to the idea was that no one had ever made it work before. Was it reasonable to condemn it on such negative grounds?

He went to the head of the physiology department, and told him the story. Dr. Miller, surprised to find his young instructor suddenly involved in the most difficult type of physiological research, listened to the recital, read the Barron article himself, and admitted that he was impressed. It was a promising research job, he told Banting. It deserved better facilities than the small laboratory of the University of Western Ontario could give it. "Go to Toronto," he told the young man. "There's a physiologist there who should hear about this—Professor Macleod. His lab is ten times better equipped than this one."

The name of John J. R. Macleod was well known to Banting. The professor, venerable in reputation if not in years, was one of Canada's most distinguished medical scientists, and his field of specialization was carbohydrate metabolism. It occurred to Banting that the procedure which seemed so novel and foolproof to him might be an old story to Macleod. But he went to Toronto.

As his old Ford chugged into town, Banting's courage began to fail him. How could he possibly sell himself to Macleod? Was there any accomplishment in his twenty-eight years to mark him out as a man of destiny? He could count the number of his patients on the fingers of one hand; to count the number of his scientific publications would take no fingers at all. Experience in physiological research? Well, he had one section of Sophomore Physiology, but he was only a few chapters ahead of the class. . . .

It is easy to see why Banting was nervous during his interview with Macleod. It is easier to see why that outspoken Scotchman turned down his request in record time. What, Macleod inquired, made Banting think that *he* could contribute anything to the study of the internal pancreatic secretions? Did he know that the method he suggested had already been tried by some of the most renowned research men in Europe? By pupils of Naunyn himself?

Banting blinked. He knew that some work had been done in the field, he said. He was not actually sure how much. . . .

Macleod snorted. Dr. Banting was not familiar with the literature of his subject? Well, for his information, plenty of work had been done by the same method. Plenty.

Banting tried a new tack. He was asking so little, he reminded Macleod. Just ten experimental animals, one assistant, a little laboratory space—and all for only eight weeks. After all, he reminded the professor casually, he *was* an alumnus.

Waste of dogs, time, and space, Macleod countered. If the method were any good, it would have worked by now. Banting, shy by nature, was too unnerved to prolong the conversation with further arguments.

He went home to London and reported failure, but he considered the matter far from closed. At Dr. Miller's suggestion he spent most of his Christmas vacation in Toronto, looking up old acquaintances of his school days. Many of them, now high in academic circles, promised to use whatever influence they had with Dr. Macleod. His second interview with the professor, however, was no more satisfactory than the first had been. The answer was still no.

Banting gave up his pursuit of a laboratory until spring. He had heard that Macleod was going home to Scotland for the summer and it occurred to him that the professor would be less antagonistic to the project if he knew that he would be a few thousand miles away from it.

The third interview was different. To Macleod's surprise, since Christmas he had been approached by a remarkable number of people who wanted to put in a good word for the unknown surgeon from Western Ontario. Yes, he told Banting, it was true that he was going away and that part of the laboratory would be unused. If Banting wanted it for a short time, he could have it. That time, Macleod suggested indirectly, was just long enough for Banting to get the idea out of his system and get himself out of the university laboratory.

Banting was pleased but not entirely satisfied. He himself could handle all the surgery involved in the experiments, he told Macleod, but he was far from proficient in chemistry. The whole project might collapse through his inability to take an accurate reading of a blood-sugar level, for example. Where could he find himself an assistant?

Macleod had a few students who were good at that sort of thing, he told Banting, and who might be foolish enough to enjoy puttering around Banting's project.

One of them was Charles Best, who had majored in physiology and bio-chemistry and who was to get his A.B. in June. Although Best usually spent his summers playing professional baseball, a pleasant enough way to help meet the expenses of the next year, he immediately declared himself in on the business. There was, of course, not a nickel of salary involved. (Banting could hardly afford to pay room rent.) But the young man seemed unconcerned by the perils of his financial affairs. He was filled with enthusiasm for the idea, and Banting would realize after the first twenty-four hours of their association that in sending Best his way, Providence had been working overtime in his favor. The young man's skill and ingenuity in running off laboratory tests of which Banting knew practically nothing awed the older man considerably. That his pre-med student colleague would turn out to be one of the most brilliant physiologists of the next generation of doctors would not come as much of a surprise to Dr. Banting.

When arrangements with Macleod and Best had been completed, Banting rushed back to London to finish out the academic year and to settle what few affairs he had. Resigning from the University, disposing of his mortgaged house and furniture, officially closing up his office—these were not very dramatic activities, but they represented a complete break with his former life. Was that, he asked himself, much of a loss? Hardly. But the process of bridge-burning naturally raised the question of what the future would hold for Banting, who was staking it on a borrowed laboratory and an idea.

The first step was easy. The plan which Banting had jotted down one night in October read: "Ligate the pancreatic ducts of dogs; wait six to eight weeks for degeneration; remove the residue and extract." Banting and Best anesthetized a few of their dogs and tied catgut ligatures around the ducts through which the digestive juices of the pancreas flow. The most irritating part of the operation was waiting the required six to eight weeks, during which time the external cells of the organ were to dry up. The two men spent the long weeks gathering and translating all the pertinent literature they could get their hands on. It was a good scientific idea, but it was a cruel blow to morale. As he read more and more of the German monographs which Best translated, Banting realized to his dismay that this specific technique really had been tried before, as Macleod had said. And it had failed. It had never been possible to isolate the internal secretion in a pure state. The experiments had been done by experts in the field of physiological research—experienced scientists who had time, money, equipment, trained assistants. It had, of course, never before been tried by an orthopedic surgeon and an undergraduate, working without funds in a borrowed laboratory which they had promised to vacate in eight weeks. That was a new angle.

Banting's frame of mind was in no way improved on the July day when he reopened the abdomens of the dogs. According to calculation, the outer cells of the pancreas should now be atrophied, giving free rein to the islets of Langerhans. One dog after another was anesthetized, opened, and examined. One dog after another had as sound a pancreas as on the day of the original operation. What had happened was immediately obvious. The catgut ligature with which Banting had tied the pancreatic ducts had simply dissolved before any effect on the cells could be felt. Of course everyone knew that catgut disintegrated quickly. This time it had done so in record time.

"My luck seems to be running true to form," Banting said, between his teeth. "It couldn't be worse."

Best growled sympathetically.

"Well——" Banting sighed. "Unless you think it would be a good idea to ditch the whole thing, we have to start all over again—with *silk* this time!"

"And with some more dogs. How were you thinking of—I mean what did you——?"

"Have in mind for money?" Banting shook his head.

"I have three dollars," Best suggested helpfully.

"To last you until September? What an extravagant life you'll be leading!" Banting frowned at the calendar, which had taken on the status of an arch-enemy. "Look at the date. I expect J. J. R. Macleod to walk through that door any minute now."

"Oh, don't worry about that. Once he gets home, he usually can't bear to tear himself away until a week before classes begin. The real problem isn't Macleod. It's funds."

Banting sighed again. "I'll have to sell something.

I can't ask my father or my brothers for another dollar."

"I can't ask mine either."

"Well, then——"

There was a long, tense silence.

"You wouldn't!" Best finally said.

"I'll have to."

He did. On a day fraught with gloom, the Ford, his last negotiable possession, and one of the few joys in his life, went off with the second-hand dealer. With the pitifully small proceeds, the two paid a little rent and bought some new supplies.

The new ligaturing operations, done with strong silk and with infinite care, were performed early in July. By the thirtieth of that month, barely four weeks later, the two decided to have a look at one of the ligated pancreases. There was a possibility that the outer cells had been at least partially destroyed by this time, and in any case, their patience was exhausted. They anesthetized one of the dogs and removed the organ. It had really felt the effects of the ligature this time, they noted with relief. The outer cells were shriveled up and had apparently lost all powers of secretion. The pancreases of the other dogs were presumably in the same condition.

Within a few days, dog Number One was exhibiting all the symptoms of diabetes. By the end of the week, he was sinking into the characteristic diabetic coma.

Samples of the dog's blood were found to be filled with sugar in amounts far above the normal level.

Quickly Banting and Best prepared for an emergency operation another dog whose pancreatic duct had been tied off. It took a remarkably short time for the surgeon to remove the pancreas of dog Number Two and for the chemist to cut the organ into tiny pieces, grind it up, and then extract the theoretically life-saving liquid from the inner cells by dissolving it in a chloride solution. The net result was a liquid which, according to their calculations, contained the pure secretion of the islets of Langerhans. Exactly what good it would do them now that they had it—*if* they had it—was matter for conjecture.

Banting filled his syringe with the extract and then injected it into the veins of the dying dog Number One. Two hours later the dog was stirring.

Three hours later the dog was conscious, completely out of the diabetic coma which had almost always before been the death warrant. Successive laboratory tests showed that the blood-sugar level was dropping to normal.

It had been a simple enough trick—after four thousand years of wondering. A good deal of luck had entered into it, for had they waited much longer before preparing the extract from the ligated pancreas of dog Number Two, their experiments would have been as fruitless as those of their predecessors. The delicate secretion of the inner cells would have been destroyed.

To Banting and Best, the brilliant success of their first experiment was cause for alarm. It was much too good to be true, a fact which they were sure their colleagues would point out to them with the greatest of pleasure. Before they could even think of disclosing their results to anyone on the outside, they must have more to show off than one dog which was barely kept alive.

In the period of frenzied activity which followed, they found that they themselves were growing with the work. From Banting, Best learned the proper surgical techniques which his colleague was developing with much skill. From Best, Banting learned the laboratory techniques with which the student felt so much at home. Soon each could do the other's work with ease. The chance combination had become a smoothly operating research team whose easy efficiency the oldest, most experienced men might envy.

Neither of them had ever worked quite so hard before. The good friends who kept a watchful eye on them knew that one or both could usually be found in the laboratory at any given hour of the twenty-four. The custom of eating three meals a day was one of the first time-consuming habits to go. Most of their food was of the sort that could be brought in by friends and reheated over a Bunsen burner. During those hectic, happy days to which Banting would one day look back with the same sort of nostalgia which Madame Curie had felt for the old shed in Rue

Lhomond, the secrets of the mysterious hormone began to unravel. They called it "isletin."

As they had feared from the start, their greatest research problem was the difficulty of keeping an appreciable amount of the stuff on hand. Eight days after his restoration to life, their favorite dog sank back into a coma and died. The supply of isletin, which had cost the lives of several companions, was finally exhausted.

The real affection which the two men felt for their dogs was, in fact, the most trying aspect of the work. The dogs themselves reciprocated in full, and their touching devotion was not always easy to take. It disturbed Banting and Best that so many dogs would have to die in order to keep one dog alive indefinitely. Now that the efficiency of their isletin had been proved to their joint satisfaction, they decided to turn all the energies of the corporation to the search for a more fruitful source of the miraculous substance.

The logical solution was the use of larger animals, and the logical place to find them was in the local meat-packing house. After a series of arduous experiments, the two worked out a method of obtaining the product from the pancreases of slaughtered cows. With this supply at their disposal, they began to gather statistics. They learned the exact quantity of isletin which resulted in maximum comfort for their canine patients; they learned that an overdose of the marvelous stuff produced its own set of disturbing symptoms which could be relieved only by feeding the dogs sugar; they worked out the proper diet to accompany the injections. Soon they had a notebook full of figures, a record complete enough to convince a professional skeptic. They soon had one on their hands.

Early in the autumn, Professor Macleod came home. He had stayed away longer than eight weeks and, fortunately, he had made no long-distance attempts to have the interlopers ejected from his laboratory in the meantime. Once back, he could hardly order Banting out of the building—not after he had seen the records which the two men had to show him. But notebooks or no notebooks, the professor had not succeeded in overcoming his original impression of the young surgeon. Having twice turned Banting down on the grounds that he was doomed to failure, he found it hard to look over the flourishing project with complete objectivity. If Macleod had thought of Banting at all during the summer, it had been with the assurance that the obnoxious young man would be effectively discouraged and out of the way by fall. It had come as something of a shock, upon entering the laboratory, to be pawed over by a whirling mass of dog flesh and to be told by the young man that several of the energetic dogs had been living comfortably without pancreases for weeks.

Faced with the evidence, Macleod's opinion was that it was interesting, but not conclusive. He called for further experiments and even put Banting and Best to work on new research problems which did not concern their own experiments. They had recently been put on a salary of sorts and accorded the official patronage both of the University and of Macleod.

Macleod, however, was a scientist, and not even his personal attitude toward Banting could prevent his scientific appreciation of the latter's work. After some weeks of delay—agonizing weeks to Banting—the professor finally concluded that isletin was quite a discovery. His only objection to the stuff, he said, was its name, the pronunciation of which would be confusing to the general public. How many people would know that the name had any connection with the word "islets," as in "islets of Langerhans," and was pronounced accordingly? Besides, he expounded, the secretion of the islets of Langerhans had been named years before its isolation, and the name had been used by several different investigators. The name was not only easier to pronounce, but it was also, more elegantly, derived from Latin. Let the product be called "insulin" from now on, Macleod ordained.

Nothing, Banting thought, could matter less to him than the superiority of the name insulin over the name isletin. What *did* matter was that while interesting but not immediately essential animal experiments were going on in Macleod's laboratory, millions of people outside the laboratory were leading the joyless lives of diabetics. Most important of all were those approaching the terminal stages of the disease, who could literally be snatched from death and restored to life by insulin. Banting had no illusions. He knew that it might take months—he hoped not years—to put insulin into commercial production. Every day lost at this end was a major catastrophe, for it meant one more day of unnecessary death.

With this unanswerable logic, Macleod agreed. And once converted, he began to expedite work on a large scale. His own time and that of his many assistants was completely given over to the new research. The tedious job of purifying and standardizing the product was largely the work of the brilliant biochemist, James B. Collip. By January 11, 1922, insulin was ready for its first public appearance.

The chief actor in this performance was a fourteen-year-old hospital patient. The boy weighed sixty-five pounds. At the outside estimate, he had about a week of life left. As Banting looked at the pale, death-shadowed face of the child, he felt his heart beat violently. The lives of so many children like this one hung on the events of the next few hours.

The boy was given insulin in gradually increasing doses, each injection followed by a complete set of tests, so that the progress of the case could be followed. In the laboratory one could read reports which showed that each injection of insulin resulted in a sharp drop of the blood-sugar level. In the sickroom, one could watch the boy's slow restoration to life.

A diabetic child who was not going to die of diabetes?

What had happened in the Toronto General Hospital in January of 1922 had never happened before in the long history of the world.

One day in February an old friend named Joseph Gilchrist came to the lab. Banting had known Dr. Gilchrist for years, and his appearance would have come as quite a shock if it had not been expected of diabetics to look that way. Dr. Gilchrist's diabetes had reached a stage in which the most rigid diet no longer helped him. He was a doctor and he was a realist. He knew that his days were sharply limited.

"I hear something fancy is going on around here," he said to Banting. "I was wondering whether you need a new rabbit."

"A rabbit?" Banting said.

"A human rabbit," Dr. Gilchrist amended.

Banting smiled slowly. "The job is yours," he said. "It starts right now." He filled a syringe without ceremony and gave his friend an immediate dose of insulin.

From that day on, Dr. Gilchrist was indeed the number-one rabbit of the laboratory. Banting, remarking on his part in the work, said later: "There is probably not a person alive who has had more samples of blood taken from his veins." Every question which the experimenters asked themselves about the proper use of insulin was answered by tests on Dr. Gilchrist's body. On the basis of his good-natured, scientific descriptions of his reaction to various insulin situations, a new chapter in the history of medicine was being written.

In the middle of that year, the newspapers got wind of the experiment. It was inevitable that some quick-witted editor would leaf through the transactions of the few medical societies to which Banting had spoken, interpret the dry, technical language of his address, and would realize that the obscure Canadian surgeon had just presented the press with the greatest human-interest story in years.

Overnight, life became a nightmare to the retiring Banting. He had yet to learn the technique of interview-dodging. He found the mass attack of the reporters a grim ordeal.

"How long does it take to cure diabetes with insulin?"

"Insulin is *not* a cure for diabetes. It's a treatment. You have to keep taking it as long as you live."

"Are you going to patent insulin and produce it for yourself?"

"Of course not!"

"What are you going to work on next, Doc?"

"I've hardly started on this."

"Dr. Banting, I want something from the woman's angle——"

"The—*what?*"

"Are you married?"

"No." He wondered whether he would have discovered insulin if he had been married, as planned.

"Can anyone get insulin now by going to the doctor and——?"

"No, no, no!"

That was the worst of it. The petty annoyance he suffered because of this invasion of his privacy was nothing. Nor did the ill will which he aroused in the gentlemen of the press matter to him. ("Banting Pearls Not For Swine" complained a headline after its paper had failed to get an interview.) The worst of the ill-timed publicity was that all over the world premature hope arose. Banting was deluged with letters from people begging for insulin, pleading with him to allow them to come to Toronto for treatment. His morning mail brought him evidence of more human misery than he had ever seen at close quarters. A brand-new industry does not spring up full-blown overnight. So far, barely enough insulin was available to keep the few experimental patients supplied. Not until 1923 did the commercial supply even begin to meet the demand.

Overwhelming as were the personal consequences of the discovery, Banting did not lose his equilibrium. His natural simplicity stood him in good stead. That he was fast becoming the social lion of Toronto alarmed him much more than it flattered him. A particularly irksome by-product of fame, he discovered, was the number of testimonial dinners which it involved. By force of will, he overcame his timidity well enough to become a competent speaker. But he could never curb his impatience with the pomposity of such gatherings.

The succession of honorary degrees, citations, decorations, and titles which came to Banting culminated in 1923 in the announcement that the discovery of insulin had been awarded the Nobel prize in medicine.

That his work had received such high tribute was gratifying, but Banting was not altogether pleased. Although the prize committee declared itself in favor of two discoverers of insulin, the other discoverer cited was John J. R. Macleod. Banting, furious that Best had been neglected in favor of Macleod, immediately announced his intention of splitting his share of the prize with his associate.

The coolness between Banting and Macleod persisted to the end. In 1928, Macleod left Toronto and returned to his native Scotland. He continued his brilliant researches on the physiology of diabetes until his death in 1935. His eventual successor to the professorship of physiology at the University of Toronto was Charles Best. Somewhere in the midst of his later work on large-scale production methods, the co-discoverer of insulin had found time to pick up an M. D. He surely qualifies as the most illustrious medical student in history.

In 1923 the University of Toronto inaugurated a new department, which it named the Banting and Best Department of Medical Research. Banting, who three years before had begged for the use of the laboratory and ten dogs, was appointed its head. "Surely," he wrote to Best, "blessings are falling on us fast enough now. We must keep our heads." They did, but one wonders how.

As chief of the new research department, in addition to his continued investigation of carbohydrate metabolism, Banting undertook valuable researches on cancer and on silicosis, one of Canada's most dangerous industrial diseases. When the war began, he turned his attention to work on a flying suit to prevent pilots from blacking out at high altitudes. On February 21, 1941, Banting took leave of the beautiful young wife he had married less than three years before and set out for England to be present at the first test run of the new equipment. He loved to fly, and the prospect of the formidable mid-winter ocean flight in a bomber delighted him, but as he left home for the airport he said to his cousin, "You know, for the first time in my life, I think I'm a little afraid." A few hours out of Newfoundland, all radio contact with his plane was lost. Four days later, a search party found the wreckage of the bomber. Three of its four passengers had been killed. Their frozen bodies, Banting's among them, were carried across the flats of the island in the sleds of a trapper.

Insulin occupies a unique position in the pharmacopeia. It has eliminated the word "hopeless" from talk about a disease of which the real cause and cure are unknown. Diabetes research is a rich field. When, how and by whom the remaining questions on the subject will be answered is still problematical. But if the second thirty years of active research bear such fruit as the first thirty did, there will be few mysteries left about the ancient disease.

8

Penicillin

THE fall of 1928 was damp. Damp Septembers were no novelty in London, which is more often wet than dry, but this year was outstandingly moist. The basement laboratory of St. Mary's Hospital was ventilated by one slightly open window through which drifted particles of dust, leaves, and other wind-blown strays calculated to turn a scientist gray before his time.

Dr. Alexander Fleming, the hospital's bacteriologist, was Scotch by birth and serene by nature. Such small hazards of laboratory life as the contamination of a fine plate of bacteria by a migratory mold did not upset him overmuch. Molds were an irritating but familiar kind of fungus which throve on the present damp weather. They were always floating in the window, picking out one's purest culture, and settling in it.

That plate of staphylococci on the laboratory bench, for example, had been a prize culture. The murderous creatures had been multiplying for all they were worth. Now it was ruined. Absently Dr. Fleming moved the plate over to the sink, turned on the water, and then glanced down at the plate. As things turned out, it was a very significant glance.

In the area immediately surrounding the stray mold the flourishing family of cocci had simply disappeared. Dr. Fleming blinked, looked again, and saw that even the colony a few inches from the invader had become transparent.

He turned off the water, took the plate back to his table, and set it down carefully. A mold flies in the window, lands in a culture, and begins to attack a colony of staphylococci. Why?

"When I saw the bacteria fading away," Dr. Fleming later said, "I had no suspicion that I had a clue to the most powerful therapeutic substance yet found to defeat bacterial infection in the human body. But the appearance of that culture plate was such that I thought it should not be neglected."

It was a happy decision for us all. The mold which Fleming grew from that original air-borne particle was a species of the Penicillium genus. The substance which it secreted to kill staphylococci the doctor named "penicillin."

Mold culture was a subject on which few bacteriologists were experts. This mold, Dr. Fleming decided, was to be treated with all the affection and understanding which he could muster. With painstaking caution, he transplanted the particle of fuzz from the culture plate, waited for it to grow into a respectably sized community, and then allowed it to simmer for two weeks in a broth. When he had filtered off the broth, he was ready to go to work.

The historic experiments of the next eight months he himself found hard to believe. And he had seen them happening with his own eyes. He could understand why the paper which he published in May of that year met with much skepticism.

Powerful? Fantastically so. Staphylococci, he found, were not the only members of the microbe world which the wandering mold conquered. In dilutions of one part to six hundred, it could also prevent the growth of streptococci and pneumococci, two of the most common man-killers known to science. Even the tough bacilli of diphtheria succumbed to it. But the microbe least affected by the broth was the weak, pallid creature which causes influenza. Quite clearly, penicillin did not work according to any set of rules yet recorded.

Dangerous? That, of course, was the question. What good was an antibacterial agent which killed a patient in the process of annihilating his germs? Dr. Fleming injected twenty cubic centimeters of penicillin broth into one rabbit, and twenty cubic centimeters of ordinary broth into another rabbit. If the two had not been labeled, he would have had no way of telling which rabbit had been given which broth. Penicillin was not toxic, at least to rabbits. It was a slight but promising bit of information.

And then what?

The problem which he now faced would be the plague of penicillin researchers for the next fourteen years. His supply of the mold was much too small. He consulted a friend, Dr. Harold Raistrick, a biologist quite capable of coping with the temperament of a cheese mold. Together the two men began an intensive campaign of penicillin growing. When they had on hand a small jealously guarded store, they began to think about finding the answer to the most important question they had yet asked themselves.

Penicillin polished off streptococci, staphylococci and pneumococci in the test-tube. It had no ill effect on laboratory animals or, as they found, on themselves. What would happen if it were actually tried on a human patient infected with streptococci, staphylococci or pneumococci?

To answer that they would have to enlist the services of some well-disposed physician with access to a hospital. They ran through a list of likely candidates. The results were unsatisfactory, but they were, at least, uniform.

"My dear fellow, how can I go around feeding my patients broth made out of mold, and expect to keep them?"

"You say this—uh—thing came in your window and landed on a plate? I see. Well—I don't think I can be of any help to you at the moment, Doctor."

"Be practical, man. Even if this stuff *is* any good, you admit yourself that you have barely enough of it on hand to treat one patient. What good will that do you? And what good will it do me if the patient happens to die? You think I'll be able to convince his relatives that he would have died anyway?"

The last argument was the convincing one. They could prove nothing about penicillin as long as it existed in such small quantities. Temporarily they gave up the doctors. But if they could interest bacteriologists or mold experts in pencillin, Fleming believed, then someone, somewhere, might come up with a solution to the problem of production. He prepared a report on a series of new laboratory experiments and presented it at a meeting of bacteriologists. In the crush of other papers, on less tenuous subjects than floating molds, the report was quietly overlooked.

The years passed, too quickly for comfort. Gradually even the few scientists who had been interested in penicillin abandoned it. The discovery, like so many discoveries before it, came dangerously close to being junked. But not quite. For ten years, Alexander Fleming kept a strain of the original mold growing in a corner of his laboratory. He was a patient man. He could wait.

By 1938 it became abundantly clear that England, and possibly the whole world, would soon be at war. And suddenly there was no longer room for apathy on such subjects as antibacterial agents. The country could look ahead to an immediate future of hospitals overflowing with wounded men. The new sulfa drugs, heralded a few years before as the cure-all for infectious diseases, had not lived up to their advance advertising. They could do a lot, but they could not begin to do everything that had been claimed for them. Of all the problems which war presented to medical researchers, none was more important than the search for an agent specifically capable of checking wound infection.

At Oxford the professor of pathology, Australian-born Howard Florey, remembered a research paper of ten years before on the properties of a common mold. He paid a visit to the now white-haired Alexander Fleming. Did the professor have any idea how or where one could locate a mold similar to the one which had drifted into his laboratory in 1928?

Dr. Fleming smiled. He had more than an idea. He had the immediate descendants of the original mold still growing in the corner of his laboratory. A strain of the mold was transferred from St. Mary's Hospital to Oxford and established in the pathology laboratory.

It was not long before Florey and his associates realized that not one word of Fleming's report on the conduct of his fungi had been an exaggeration. By the time the routine laboratory work had been done, they were convinced that penicillin was a test-tube sensation. Would it prove successful in action?

Florey isolated eight white mice and proceeded to shoot them full of the most vicious strain of staphylococci he could get his hands on. Four of the unlucky eight were left alone; four were given shots of penicillin every three hours, for one day and one night. By morning, four mice were dead and four mice were alive and mending. So far penicillin was batting a thousand.

"It can save people as well as mice," Florey thought, but he made his first tests with little enthusiasm. There was unfortunately a catch to penicillin.

From their very first animal experiments, the Oxford men had been aware of one unhappy feature about their mold-broth. The body does not retain penicillin. It is thrown out almost as quickly as it can be forced in. "It is like pouring water down a basin with the plug out," Florey said later. The amount necessary to keep four mice alive for twenty-four hours had almost depleted the laboratory supply. How could they scrape together an amount large enough to treat a man? What, for that matter, did they hope to prove by treating a patient with penicillin? The merits of a substance which existed in quantities just large enough to cure four mice were of questionable interest to practical people. Men were dying by the thousands and were being wounded by the tens of thousands in 1940.

In February of that year a London policeman cut his face while shaving. It was a common enough accident but, as it developed, a particularly unfortunate one. Two weeks later, the man was dying of blood poisoning, his body invaded by a horde of vicious staphylococci against which sulfa preparations had proved no more effective than a wooden gun against cannon fire.

The case so obviously was made to order for their purposes that Florey and his associates could not let it go by. Every available bit of penicillin in the laboratory was marshalled and moved over to the Radcliffe Infirmary of Oxford. The dying man was given a dose of penicillin injected directly into the blood stream every three hours. Five days passed—or crawled, as it seemed to Florey. Within two days a slight drop in temperature was recorded; on the third day, the horrible swellings on the man's face began to subside. The next day his temperature was close to normal, and by the fifth day, his recovery seemed assured. But by then the last fleck of penicillin was gone.

Back in the laboratory, heart-breaking efforts were being made to scrape together a new supply of the mold. It came too late. Before the treatments could be resumed the infection had made headway, and the man died.

By practical standards, the first trial of penicillin had been a failure, since the patient was dead. Actually, those who had seen the progress of the case were thoroughly convinced that their preoccupation with an air-borne mold was a good idea after all. They worked on the cultivation of a new batch, and chafed for the opportunity to use it.

The telephone rang early one morning. . . "Florey? This is Fletcher. I have a case here I think you might like to look at. Fifteen-year-old boy—terrific hemolytic strep infection. . . Sulfas? No. Couldn't do a thing for it. I don't give him another forty-eight hours to live, unless——"

The second time it happened. A patient who should have been dead within forty-eight hours, by all existing standards, stayed alive. Once again the supply of penicillin was exhausted, but this time it had held out just long enough.

"Now," Florey thought, "we have to stop fooling around. We have to get more of the stuff. . . " Production, he knew, was a problem for experienced drug manufacturers, not for a pathology laboratory. How did one go about convincing a drug company of so obvious a fact?

It was a vicious circle. Penicillin research had reached a stage at which it demanded large-scale, wholesale experimenting in clinics all over the world. So far, enough of the precious stuff had been produced to treat two patients—one unsuccessfully. Unless the drug were manufactured by the ton, not by the teaspoon, such experimenting could never be done. Yet what drug manufacturer in his right mind could be expected to say, "Certainly, Doctor, I will gladly spend a few million to set up production of this unknown drug which has failed so far in fifty per cent of the cases in which it has been tried." No, Florey reasoned, he had to have more figures. He had to have records which would appeal to the sales manager of a drug company as well as to its laboratory director.

But how? It was a project which would demand the full time, interest and loyalty of an expert physician. Florey and his associates were barely able to keep the laboratory going, much less take up the practice of medicine. But how could they possibly find a doctor willing and able to drop his heavy wartime burdens simply to hold up the medical end of their half-baked research project? On the surface it was an impossible order. But Florey's uncommon luck did not desert him. He had the answer to the problem in his own house.

Ethel Florey was a gentle-faced housewife, the mother of two children who had recently been evacuated to the United States. But she was also a doctor. She had studied and practiced in Australia for some years before coming to England and settling down to the job of being a doctor's wife. When her husband announced to her that she was now back in practice, the information came as something of a shock. She had been away from medicine and medical techniques for years, she reminded Florey. Now he was asking her to plunge into a field of practice so new that there were not even any established rules to learn. Did he really think she could do it?

Did she have anyone else to suggest for the job, her husband queried? It was not an answer to her question, but it made the point. His project was simple enough in outline, Florey explained. He and his associates would stay in the laboratory and would devote their concerted efforts to the growing of molds and the brewing of penicillin. From there on the responsibility was hers.

It was quite a responsibility. To pick out cases most likely to prove the efficacy of the drug, to watch over every milligram of it as one might guard gold dust on its way to the mint, to bring in reports of undeviating accuracy, calculated to arouse the good will of drug-company stockholders. . . Ethel Florey packed the priceless few grams into sterilized cold-cream jars, put the cold-cream jars into an old vanity case strapped onto her bicycle, and set out for the Radcliffe Infirmary. There was a case in residence which interested her—a girl dying of a fatal streptococcus infection. In the same hospital there was a two-months-old baby, its spine twisted, its whole body aflame with osteomyelitis, one of the most vicious and incurable of all infections. Although Ethel Florey had hardly dared hope for it, both these patients recovered after being treated with penicillin. So did the empyema, streptococcus meningitis, the bacterial endocarditis and the septicemia patients whom she elected as her test cases. By the end of the year, the cooperative effort of the Flory household had resulted in 187 carefully documented reports of penicillin therapy. Florey felt that it was time to put penicillin into production on a vast scale. It was a big order, and there was only one possible place to fill it.

In July of 1941, Howard Florey and his colleague, Dr. Norman Heatley, arrived in the United States carrying with them a sample of the mold descended from Dr. Fleming's strain. Penicillin was about to enter the third phase of its spectacular career. From here on its destiny was in the experienced hands of American industry.

Doctors Florey and Heatley were barely off the ship before they found themselves hustled onto a train and headed, of all places, for Peoria. There the Fermentation Division of the Northern Regional Research Laboratory knew a good mold when it saw one. In no time at all, Florey and Heatley had sold the Division on penicillin. Now they waited to see whether the recalcitrant creature would grow with more enthusiasm in Peoria than it had in Oxford.

The penicillium growers at Oxford had used as a growing medium a solution containing certain minerals and glucose. The yields from this medium had been discouragingly low, as we have seen. One liter of medium had usually yielded not more than 1000 units of penicillin. And it took 100,000 units to treat a case of blood poisoning for one day!

The practical Americans came to grips with the problem at once. "We find some new way to grow the stuff, or we forget all about it," they decided. They inaugurated a systematic search for a better medium.

It was Dr. A. J. Moyer who pulled the much-needed rabbit out of the hat. One day a routine check of his flasks showed that one of them was producing 200 units of penicillin to every cubic centimeter. *Two hundred thousand* to a liter instead of 1000 to a liter! The medium which had so intoxicating an effect on the mold? Simple, home-brewed corn-steep liquor.

The jinx was broken. With production yields up two hundred times almost over night, the drug manufacturers began to take notice. Firms which had said, "Sorry, not interested," now announced a desire to discuss terms. One by one, the leading firms of the country added the new product to their lists. And all over the country, chemists, bacteriologists, engineers, government officials and medical-research men were sitting up late over their notebooks and their test-tubes.

The cooperative venture paid off in units of penicillin. In 1943, during the first five months of commercial production, 400,000,000 units of the severely rationed product were turned out. By the end of the year, the figure had jumped to 9,194,000,000 units a month. From that day on, the figures began multiplying themselves in astronomic proportion. In late 1948, eight million million units of pure crystalline penicillin were rolling out of the laboratories every month. The names of all the people who made such figures possible are impossible to list. But they all belong to the story.

While doctors worked out the refinements of penicillin therapy, puzzled over ways to combat the inevitable penicillin allergies, and pitted their wits against those super-microbes which began learning how to combat the drug, a vast new research enterprise was springing up all over the world.

If nature had concealed so powerful a weapon in a humble wind-blown mold, then it was entirely possible that she had tucked others away in equally unlikely places. The most commonplace bits of matter, easily available in almost any back yard, were suddenly subjected to scrutiny. The results have been making headlines for six years: aureomycin, bacitracin, chloromycetin, polymyxin, and many others. These antibiotics—a name given to living organisms which have the power to kill bacteria—are such recent discoveries that their full usefulness is not really known. But many of them seem to destroy a growing list of bacteria against which penicillin is powerless.

In 1943 one such routine search for molds was under way at Rutgers University in New Jersey. Dr. Selman A. Waksman had mapped out a program as ambitious as any yet attempted by a hunter of antibiotics. He was on the trail of a substance to combat a penicillin-resistant class of organisms called "Gram-negative" because of their staining properties. In particular he wanted something which could destroy the vicious bacillus of tuberculosis.

Waksman realized that finding such an antibiotic among the innumerable products which he planned to test would probably take him the rest of his life, if indeed he ever found it at all. Neither he nor any other good scientist could have believed that he would come upon what he wanted after only three months of research.

During a routine check of a strain called *Streptomyces griseus,* Waksman discovered that it seemed active against certain Gram-negative bacteria. In keeping with laboratory routine, but with no premonition of success, he tried out the strain on a culture of tuberculosis bacilli. To his utter amazement he found that the mold liquidated the tuberculosis germs.

The next few weeks were the most exciting ones the normally calm Rutgers laboratory had ever known. Streptomycin, as the new mold was called, was even more of a laboratory show-off than penicillin had been. In the test-tube it killed the organisms causing tuberculosis, undulant fever, whooping cough, tularemia, pneumonia and some forms of dysentery.

Is streptomycin a cure for tuberculosis in the body as well as in the test-tube? No one knows the answer. Dr.

Waksman himself, alarmed by the effusions of the press, said in a radio broadcast: "Great caution must be exercised in extending the hope that a cure for tuberculosis has finally been found!" A complete cure for tuberculosis is probably still in the future. But streptomycin, with its astounding record in experiments performed at the Mayo Clinic and by the Army Medical Corps, represents the most promising step yet taken towards its conquest.

The great organic chemists of the last century and the early years of this one looked for remedies in the man-made molecules of synthetic drugs. They would have been surprised to learn that their followers would devote their energies to such items as molds, soy beans and garlic, searching out the remedies provided by nature herself for curing human disease. But modern scientists are not really doing anything new. They are, quite literally, getting down to earth.